My Fun with Learning

My Fun Book

by

Jack B. Long

The Southwestern Company

Nashville, Tennessee

About the Author

For 40 years Jack B. Long has been engaged in creating books for pre-schoolers and beginning readers. He was an elementary schoolteacher—primary and middle grades—for five years.

In 1951, after working in Kansas City, Missouri, as a writer and editor for Hallmark greeting cards' juvenile line, Long joined Tell-Well Press, also in Kansas City, as a member of their editorial department. Success there with read-to books, such as *Little Squeegy Bug* for the very young, and with a pre-school series, led him to Western Publishing Company in New York City, where he worked for over 20 years as writer and editor in their juvenile division. Long was responsible for many of Western's Little Golden Books, enjoyed by countless numbers of small children. While there, he worked closely with Louis Untermeyer on *Poems for the Very Young* and authored a large number of read-to books, among them *The Happy, Healthy Pooh Book, Tiny Bear Goes to the Fair,* and a twelve-title series of beginning readers. He also created for the juvenile education department *Getting Your Child Ready to Read* and *The First Big Step—Getting Ready for School.*

ACKNOWLEDGMENTS:

TEXT

"I Don't Want to Play in Your Yard," an 1894 song, words
by Philip Wingate, music by H. W. Petrie.

ILLUSTRATIONS

Ilil Arbel	pp. 26–39, 41–45, 82–85, 156–157, 164–165
Kim Mulkey	pp. 68–73, 150–155, 158–159, 162–163, 166–167
Jo Polseno	pp. 130–137, 140–143
Yuri Salzman	pp. 46–61, 86–111, 182–191
Leonard Shortall	pp. 40, 80–81, 112–129, 168–181
Walter Velez	pp. 6–25, 62–67, 138–139
Ron Walotsky	pp. 74–79
Patricia J. Wynne	pp. 146–149, 160–161

Produced by The Hudson Group, Inc.
Designed by Carlo De Lucia

A Note for Parents

The purpose of *My Fun Book* is to reveal the joy of becoming acquainted with the importance of words. It is a first giant step in reading readiness. This book and the ones that follow guide both children and parents along the wonderful path that is a journey to knowledge.

My Fun Book presents the basics of learning in a stimulating and fun-loving fashion. There is the time-honored alphabet. There are the nursery rhymes that represent part of our rich heritage. There are the all-important counting exercises. Stories, riddles, games, and puzzles delight, motivate, and instruct.

My Fun Book is a book to grow into and to grow with. Each section or unit contains something for the very young child just beginning to take the first steps toward learning as well as something for the older child who is being caught up in the wonder-filled quest for information.

This, of course, is a sharing book. Parents are always the first teachers, so this is a guide book for them. Each unit concludes with a "Note to Parents" that stresses the importance of the material in the section and adds suggestions that enrich as well as add fun while parents and their children share the adventure of learning.

This is also a book for prereaders and beginning readers. Each of the units has its specific purpose; all the units together represent a reading readiness program. "The Alphabet" and "Fun with Words" are designed specifically to promote reading readiness. "Going Places" introduces awareness of the environment and uses street and road signs to promote reading. "About Colors," with its red, green, yellow, blue, orange, and purple pages, not only delights the eye but emphasizes the importance of color in everyday life. "Do's and Don'ts," a manners and safety section, lightens the seriousness of the subject with humor. "You and Your Friends" and "You and Your Pets" teach through example the essential art of getting along with others and with animals. "The Seasons" is a beginner's introduction to the year's calendar, with special highlights for the holidays enjoyed by parents and children. "Shapes and Numbers" makes counting fun as well as meaningful. It makes a game of learning basic shapes through riddles, jokes, and stories that are fun and enlightening.

This book provides parents and children alike with a wonderful adventure. The eagerness of children to know more, to reach out, to question, and to press forward should always be encouraged. *My Fun Book* is a beginning tour guide to the main highways and the fascinating byways of learning. Sharing this knowledge and encouraging learning by children will be one of life's richest rewards.

Jack B. Long

CONTENTS

My Fun Book

An Alphabet Tr

A B

H I J K

Q R S T U

6

ith Sally and Sam

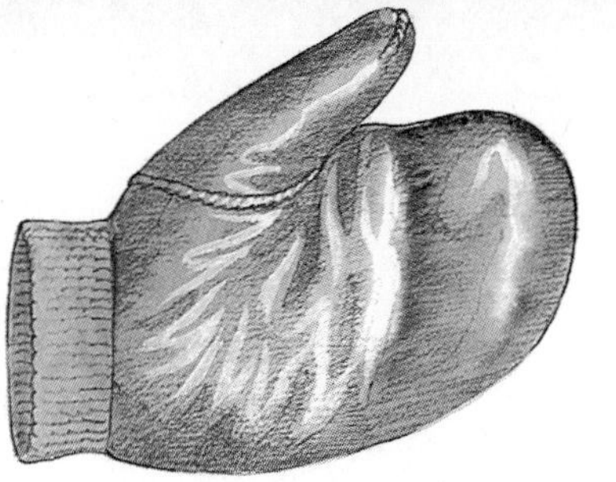

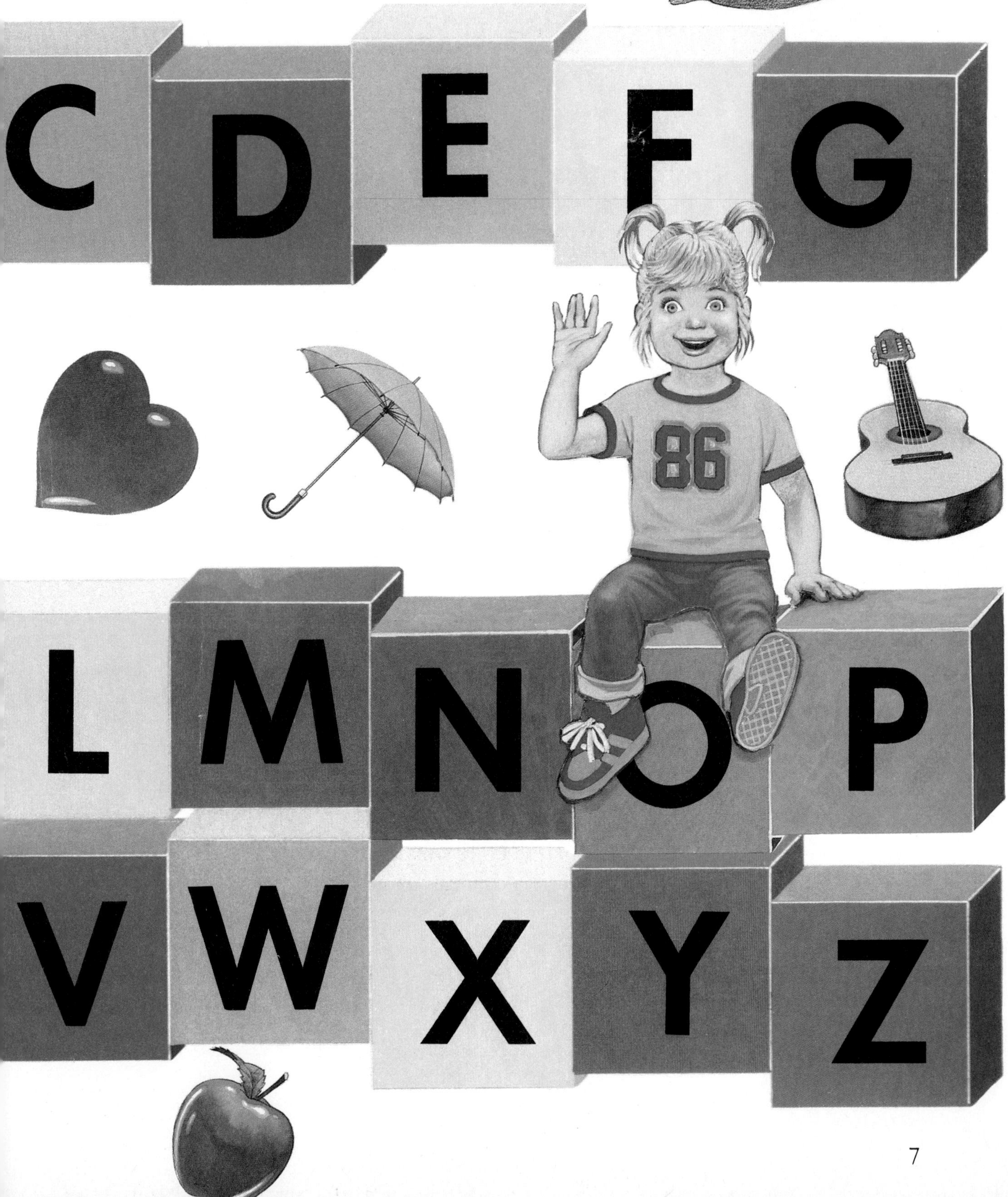

C D E F G

L M N O P

V W X Y Z

A is for <u>Airplane</u>.

See how it flies.

B is for <u>Birthday</u>—

A <u>Big Birthday</u> surprise!

Happy Birthday to you,
  Happy Birthday to you,
Happy Birthday dear Sally,
  Happy Birthday to you.

C is for <u>Cake</u>.

For <u>Candles</u> bright too.

How many <u>Candles</u>

Should there be for you?

D
is for <u>Ducks</u>. As swimmers they are best.

E
is for <u>Eggs</u>. Safe and snug in the nest.

F

is for <u>Fiddle</u> played by the cat.

Hey, diddle, diddle!

That cat is so <u>Fat</u>.

11

G is for <u>Gate</u> that Sam stands beside.

H is for <u>Horse</u>. <u>He</u> is going to ride.

I is for Ice cream so good to eat.

When the weather is hot,

A wonderful treat.

J

is for <u>J</u>ack and <u>J</u> is for <u>J</u>ill

The boy and the girl who went

up the hill.

Oh! Oh! What happened?

Did something spill?

K is for <u>Kitten</u> as everyone knows.

L is for <u>Ladybug</u>

That <u>Lands</u> on her nose.

M is for <u>Mealtime</u>.

Now do not be late!

N is for <u>Napkin</u>.

Beside every plate.

O is for <u>Owl</u> and <u>Opossum</u> so shy.

P is for <u>Porcupine</u> living close by.

Q is for <u>Quack</u>

The sound that ducks make.

They all say, "Quack, quack"

While they swim in a lake.

R is for <u>Rhino</u>.

Oh my! what a pet.

S is for <u>Sam</u>

And for <u>Sally</u>, you bet.

T

is for <u>Timmy's Turtle</u>

Who's really very slow,

And <u>Takes</u> his house along

with him

Wherever he may go.

U is for <u>Umbrella</u>

To <u>Use</u> in spring showers.

V is for <u>Violets</u>—those pretty spring flowers.

W

is for <u>Wet Water</u>

As <u>Walruses</u> all know.

X

marks the spot

Where the <u>Xylophone</u> should go.

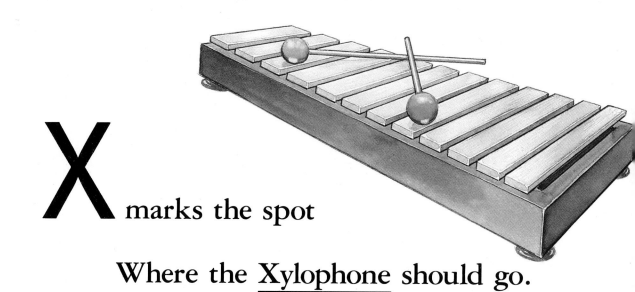

Y

is for <u>Yo-Yo</u> and <u>Yummy</u> <u>Yogurt</u>, too.

Z

is for <u>Zebra</u>. He lives at the <u>Zoo</u>.

Alphabet Parade
The Bigs and the Littles

Aa Bb Cc Dd

Ee Ff Gg Hh

Ii Jj Kk Ll

Mm Nn Oo Pp

Qq Rr Ss Tt

U u V v W w

X x Y y Z z

NOTE TO PARENTS

Here are some alphabet facts you may want to share with your children. The alphabet has 26 letters.

The early alphabet was made up only of capital letters. Small letters came about when writers started rounding off the large letters to save time and space.

To acquaint your children with the alphabet, you can play games by putting letters together to form their names. You also can draw or cut out pictures of familiar objects and then print the words for them underneath. Should your children ask what certain words mean, show them how words can be looked up and explained in a dictionary.

The Shape Family

I am one of the best known members of the Shape family. My name is *square*. See my four straight sides. All of them are the same size. You see me many times each day.

A cracker is a square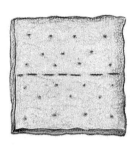

A window can be a square

And square pans

There are square cans

Can you think of other square things?

Here are two "square" riddles.

The answer to each riddle is a square shape.

> You put your toys inside me
> When you pick them up each day,
> And then you'll always find them
> When it's time again to play.

> We're made of plastic or of wood.
> We're always shaped the same,
> And anytime you play with us,
> You play a building game.

28

Hello! My name is *triangle*. I have three straight sides. Sometimes all three of my sides are the same length. Sometimes they are different. Sometimes I am good to eat.

A piece of pie
   is a triangle

Quite often a sandwich
      is in the shape
      of a triangle

Some tents can be shaped like triangles.
Some sails on sailboats are triangles.
When you draw the top of a mountain,
it looks like a triangle.
If you see a triangle in the sky, it is
probably a kite.

Can you think of other triangle shapes?

29

I am a friendly shape. You can go round and round with me. My name is *circle*.

The wheels on wagons and cars are circles

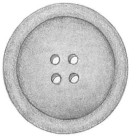

Many buttons are circles

And so are cookies

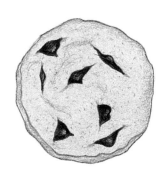

When the moon is a circle, we call it a full moon.
How many things can you name that are circle shapes?

Here are two "circle" riddles.

The answer to each riddle is a circle shape.

Through the night and through the day,
I always go tick-tock.
I try my best to be on time.
I am, of course, a _____ .

My face is round and I wear a grin,
And the time I'm usually seen
Is by candlelight on a scary night
That's known as Halloween.

Fun with Shapes

Ask your mother or father to draw you some squares, triangles, and circles. They should be different sizes. Maybe you will want to color them.

If you or your parents cut the shapes out, you can put them together to make a number of things:

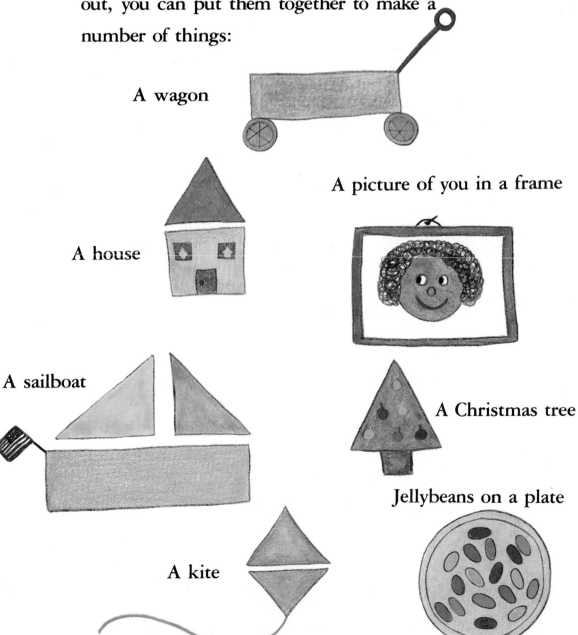

A wagon

A picture of you in a frame

A house

A sailboat

A Christmas tree

Jellybeans on a plate

A kite

One to Ten

When Sally goes to the library, there are ten steps to climb that lead to the big double door. She always counts them.

Can you count them too?

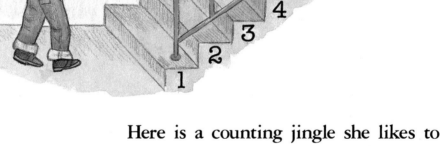

Here is a counting jingle she likes to say when she climbs the ten steps.

One, two, buckle my shoe.
Three, four, shut the door.
Five, six, pick up sticks.
Seven, eight, lay them straight.
Nine, ten, a big fat hen.

And Back Again . . .

When Sally comes out of the library with the books she has picked out, she likes to count from ten back again.

Can you count with her?

Sometimes Sally and her friend Debbie race to see who can get to the end of the block first. So that they both start at the same time, they say this counting jingle.

One for the money, two for the show,
Three to make ready, four to go!

A Number Parade

Here is my picture. **1** Here is my name. **one**

Here is my picture. **2** Here is my name. **two**

Here is my picture. **3** Here is my name. **three**

Here is my picture. **4** Here is my name. **four**

Here is my picture. **5** Here is my name. **five**

Here is my picture. **6** Here is my name. **six**

Here is my picture. **7** Here is my name. **seven**

Here is my picture. **8** Here is my name. **eight**

Here is my picture. **9** Here is my name. **nine**

Here is my picture. **10** Here is my name. **ten**

1	2	3	4	5
one	two	three	four	five
6	7	8	9	10
six	seven	eight	nine	ten

Some More Shapes

Here are more interesting shapes.

This shape is a *crescent*. Look for it in the sky when there is a new moon.

This is a *star* shape. You sometimes find it on top of a Christmas tree.

These next shapes have long names. All the names have to do with how many sides the shapes have.

This is a *pentagon*. Did you count five sides?

This is a *hexagon*. It has six sides.

This shape has eight sides. It is called an *octagon*.

There are *heart* shapes and *diamond* shapes too.

How Many?

Long ago, people found out that they needed a way to remember how many things they owned. At first, of course, there were no words for counting. Probably, people used sticks or stones to count.

If they had a herd of goats, for instance, they would use one stick to stand for each goat. Then when they brought the herd in for milking, they could tell by matching sticks against goats whether or not any goats were missing.

This took time, so before long people made up counting words. The big difference was that the counting words had to be used in order. "One" came before "two" and "three" came before "four." With sticks it had not mattered.

Since people are always looking for the quickest way to do things, numbers were invented to stand for the counting words. The number 1 stood for the word "one," 2 stood for "two," and so on. It was much faster.

So, down through the years a parade of numbers to tell us *how many* has come forth. And it is the numbers that are the easiest and quickest to use.

one

1

Over in the Meadow

Over in the meadow in the sand in the sun
Lived an old mother turtle and her little turtle *one*.
"Dig," said the mother. "We dig," said the *one*.
So they dug all day in the sand in the sun.

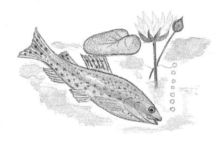

Over in the meadow where the stream runs blue
Lived an old mother fish and her little fishes *two*.
"Swim," said the mother. "We swim," said the *two*.
So they swam all day where the stream runs blue.

Over in the meadow in a hole in a tree
Lived an old mother owl and her little owls *three*.
"Tu-whoo," said the mother. "Tu-whoo," said the *three*.
So they tu-whooed all day in a hole in a tree.

Over in the meadow by the old barn door
Lived an old mother rat and her little ratties *four*.
"Gnaw," said the mother. "We gnaw," said the *four*.
So they gnawed all day by the old barn door.

Over in the meadow in a snug beehive
Lived an old mother bee and her little bees *five*.
"Buzz," said the mother. "We buzz," said the *five*.
So they buzzed all day in a snug beehive.

Over in the meadow in a nest built of sticks
Lived an old mother crow and her little crows *six*.
"Caw," said the mother. "We caw," said the *six*.
So they cawed all day in a nest built of sticks.

Over in the meadow where the grass grows so even
Lived an old mother frog and her little froggies *seven*.
"Jump," said the mother. "We jump," said the *seven*.
So they jumped all day where the grass grows so even.

Over in the meadow by the old mossy gate
Lived an old mother lizard and her little lizards *eight*.
"Bask," said the mother. "We bask," said the *eight*.
So they basked all day by the old mossy gate.

Over in the meadow by the old Scotch pine
Lived an old mother duck and her little ducks *nine*.
"Quack," said the mother. "We quack," said the nine.
So they quacked all day by the old Scotch pine.

Over in the meadow in a cozy wee den
Lived an old mother beaver and her little beavers *ten*.
"Beave," said the mother. "We beave," said the *ten*.
So they beaved all day in a cozy wee den.

Measuring Words

Here are some questions that are answered with *measuring* words:

How much do you weigh?

The scale you stand on will show you in *pounds* and *ounces*.

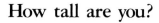

How tall are you?

The measuring tape, ruler, or yardstick will show you in *feet* and *inches*.

How far have you gone in the car?

The odometer will show you in *miles*.

How much milk is there in the refrigerator?

The containers will probably be in *pint*, *quart*, *half-gallon*, or *gallon* sizes.

A Little Bit About Money

A piggy bank is where you can keep your money.

A store is where you can spend your money.

Money comes in the round shape of coins made of metal.

There is also paper money called bills.

Learning to count money is important because it is nice to know how much you are saving, or how much you have to spend.

Let us meet the Money family

My name is *penny*. I am also called one-cent piece. I am copper colored. Although I cannot buy much, it is nice to save me because pennies add up. Five of me will buy as much as the next member of the Money family.

Hello! My name is *nickel*. I am also called five-cent piece. I am silver colored. Two of me will buy just as much as the next family member.

My name is *dime*. I am also called ten-cent piece. Although I am smaller in size than nickel, I am worth two times as much. I am the same color, but usually shinier.

Hi, there. I am *quarter*, the next member of the Money family. I am also called twenty-five cent piece. You will find "Quarter Dollar" printed on me.

My name is *half dollar*. I am larger than quarter and I can buy twice as much. Sometimes I am called fifty-cent piece. You will find "Half Dollar" printed on me.

I am the largest of the silver coins because I am worth the most. My name is *dollar*. Since I weigh a lot, most people would rather carry one-dollar bills made of paper. They buy the same amount.

The Money family is really large. There are five-dollar, ten-dollar, twenty-dollar bills, and on up.

Here is a coin money family tree to show how many of each one of us coins it takes to make a dollar.

Have fun counting us.

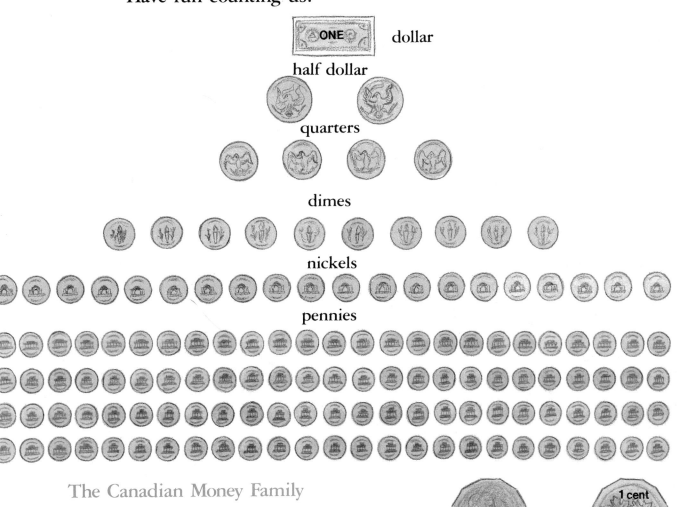

dollar

half dollar

quarters

dimes

nickels

pennies

The Canadian Money Family

Here are our Canadian cousins in the Money family. The names are mostly similar, but the coins and paper bills look a little different.

Canadian
Pennies

Playing Store

It is fun to play store. First, you and your friends get some empty packages or boxes. (Your mothers or fathers can save these for you as they use up whatever is in them.) Next, place the empty boxes on a bench, table, or chairs. This is your store. Pretend that this box costs a nickel, that box a dime, another a quarter. Maybe this big box costs a dollar, or even two dollars.

If you have some play money around, that is fine. If you do not, make your own money out of paper or cardboard. Mother or Dad might help you trace some pennies, nickels, dimes, quarters, half dollars, and dollars on paper. Then together you can cut them out and label them.

Now find a larger box. A shoe box would be fine. It will be your cash register. You will want to put some of your money in the cash register so the person at the cash register can take a customer's money and make change if necessary. Each customer should have enough money to shop with. Some make-believe paper money, in the form of dollar bills or even five-dollar bills, is a good idea.

Now you are ready to play store. Enjoy yourselves!

NOTE TO PARENTS

Shapes and Numbers is an early introduction to simple arithmetic. Becoming acquainted with numbers and what they stand for is an important learning experience. Recognizing shapes and sizes is a visual part of learning in this area. Just hearing the special vocabulary of arithmetic is helpful.

Counting should be taught by concept. When people first began to count things, they probably used their fingers. This is still a good one-to-ten method. Recognizing the various money units and understanding their value is another important step for children.

Above all, do not rush this learning process. Repetition is necessary and so is patience. Learning should never be a chore for children. Help make it an adventure.

Rainbow Rhymes and Songs

Rainbow, rainbow, way up high
Your colors number seven.
From the earth up to the sky
Like a bridge to heaven.

When there's rainbow overhead,
After April showers,
It's like a special promise
Of pretty Maytime flowers.

In the jungles far away,
When the rains stop by-and-by,
The people call the rainbow
"Pretty window in the sky."

Sliding down a rainbow
From way up in the sky—
What a lot of fun to watch
The colors whizzing by!

46

When little Miss Martha,
As pretty as can be,
Wore a lovely rainbow coat,
She was a sight to see.

Anytime you see a rainbow
Here is what you do—
Make a very special wish,
And hope that it comes true.

Sally's Garden

Sally's favorite color was red. She loved red apples and red strawberries. She liked to look at red sunsets. Her grandmother's red roses were the flowers that she liked best. "I wish everything were red," she said to herself.

Early one spring Sally said to her mother, "May I have a red flower garden?"

"You want to grow only red flowers?" her mother asked.

Sally nodded.

So Sally and her mother planted red flowers—red tulips, red asters, red dahlias, and red petunias. They set out red rosebushes and red geraniums.

Sally watched the flowers grow. It seemed to take them such a long time. The bright red tulips were the first to bloom. "How pretty!" Sally exclaimed.

Then, one by one, the other flowers bloomed. The blossoms were different shapes and different sizes, but they all looked pretty much the same.

"I wish now," Sally told her mother,
"that I had planted some blue, and yellow,
and orange flowers. Red is nice, but I like
it best when it is mixed in with other colors."

The Blue Page

Little Boy Blue,
Come blow your horn.
The sheep's in the meadow.
The cow's in the corn.

But where is the boy
That looks after the sheep?
He's under a haystack,
Fast asleep.

Oh, dear, what can the matter be?
Johnny's so long at the fair.
He promised to buy me a bunch of blue
     ribbons
To tie up my bonnie brown hair.

How do you like to go up in a swing,
Up in the air so blue?
Oh, I do think it is the pleasantest thing
Ever a child can do!

from "The Swing"
by Robert Louis Stevenson

Sam and the Green Things

"There's nothing to do," Sam complained. "Sally is visiting her cousin. My other friends are gone for the weekend." Sam had just finished breakfast, and the day stretching ahead seemed it might last forever.

"Well, Sam," his father said, "I'm going to paint some outdoor things. Maybe you can find something to paint, too. But they have to be green things. That's the only color of paint I have."

"How about your toy box?" Sam's mother asked. "And your swing seat? They both need new coats of paint, and green will do just fine."

"And the birdhouse Dad made for me," Sam added. "I can paint it green."

The day ahead seemed exciting now. So Sam put on old clothes that a few spots of paint would not hurt. His father gave him a brush just the right size and a small bucket of green paint.

"Be very careful," his father said. He painted a little bit of Sam's toy box to show him how.

"Don't put too much paint on your brush and go slowly."

Sam liked to paint. It was special fun to cover scratches with the green paint. The swing board looked fine. He was almost finished painting when he tipped over the paint bucket.

"Oh! Oh!" said Sam.

"Don't worry,'" his father said. "You have enough paint left to finish the birdhouse."

When Sam was done, his hands were almost as green as the birdhouse.

"We'll clean off the paint in a jiffy," his mother said.

Painting things had been fun!
And green was a wonderful color.

A birdie with a yellow bill

Hopped upon the window sill

Cocked his shining eye and said:

"Aren't you 'shamed, you sleepyhead?"

Robert Louis Stevenson

Little Yellow Bird

Little Yellow Bird was a busy bird. Every morning she had many people to awaken.

There was the old woman in the shoe who had so many children she didn't know what to do. There was Daffy-Down-Dilly in her yellow petticoat and green gown who had to get to town early. There was Yellow Butterfly who stayed in a tree with yellow apples. There were the three little yellow kittens that were always losing their mittens.

When the yellow sun peeked over the edge of Big Meadow, Little Yellow Bird started her rounds. "Wake up, you sleepyheads," she chirped.

One morning Little Yellow Bird was very surprised. No one was at home. The old woman and all her children were gone. Daffy-Down-Dilly had left. Yellow Butterfly was not in the tree with yellow apples. The three yellow kittens were missing too.

"What has happened?" Little Yellow Bird said, and

she flew in circles calling to her friends. No one answered.

Then, from behind trees and bushes, all her friends appeared. They had been waiting to surprise her.

"It's a thank-you party, Little Yellow Bird," Daffy-Down-Dilly told her, "because you've been so helpful waking us morning after morning."

The Orange Page

Orange is a color
As bright as can be.
How many orange things
Do you see?

The Purple Page

I never saw a Purple Cow.

I never hope to see one;

But I can tell you, anyhow,

I'd rather see than be one!

Gelett Burgess

How many purple things can you find on this page?

Color Puzzles

Many animals use color to play a sort of hide-and-seek game.

The animals become color puzzles. Sometimes their colors and the colors of things around them help hide them from other animals that might hurt them.

White polar bears are hard to see against the white snow where they live. Hunters often do not see them.

Some animals even change colors. The snowshoe hare wears a white coat in the winter. When summer, comes he changes to a brown coat.

The picture shows different animals and insects making color puzzles of themselves. How many can you find? Here's a hint.

There are five of them hiding in the picture.

Look for a speckled bird that matches the leaves and grass around it.

Look for a green frog hiding among the leaves.

Look for a desert lizard that is colored very like the sand and pebbles where he lives.

Look for the butterfly on the tree trunk.

Can you find the screech owl? It looks like the tree.

Try looking for color puzzles outdoors.

59

Fun with Color

Make a color patchwork. Tear out shapes in colored construction paper. Paste them so they overlap on a big sheet of paper.

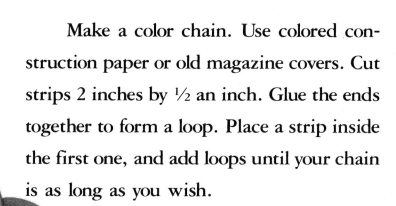

Make a color chain. Use colored construction paper or old magazine covers. Cut strips 2 inches by ½ an inch. Glue the ends together to form a loop. Place a strip inside the first one, and add loops until your chain is as long as you wish.

Draw a picture with many colored lines, circles, and scrawls. Large, fat crayons are easiest to draw with.

Play a color game with a friend. Look around the room and say, "I see something blue." Then ask your friend to guess what

60

it is. When it is your friend's turn, your friend will say, "I see something green." Now you look and guess. When you cannot find any other colors, start over again with blue.

NOTE TO PARENTS

The sooner you introduce color to your children, the better. When you are out walking, for example, point out the color of various things. Watch sunsets with your children. Talk about favorite colors. Train your children to look about and to observe.

Nature walks are wonderful color tours. Picture storybooks are treasuries of bright, bold colors. Buying balloons can be an exercise in color selection. Ask your children which color balloon to buy.

Why was that color chosen? Why do some colors seem cool and others, like red, seem warm?

If there is a black and white picture illustrating a story, ask your children to imagine the different colors that might be painted in. Keep their rooms bright with color.

Sam Visits His Grandmother

"There's a letter for you, Sam," the postman said and handed him the mail.

"Thank you," Sam replied, and ran with the mail to the kitchen where his mother was making lunch.

She looked through the letters. "Here's one for you. It's from your grandmother." She opened it and read:

Dear Sam,

We're spending the summer at the beach. Your grandfather stays in the city during the week to be near his office. I get lonely. Ask your mother and father whether you can come visit me. We can have lots of fun together, and at the next cottage there are children about your age. Tell your mother to call me if you can come. On the weekend your grandfather will take you out in the boat and you can fish.

Love,
Grandma

"Please, may I go?" Sam asked his mother. "Let's see what your father says," his mother said.

That evening, after his dad had agreed it was a wonderful idea, they called Sam's grandmother. She was very happy that Sam was coming to see her. "I'll meet the bus at Seaside City," she said. "Sam, we'll have a great time."

Sure enough, Grandma was waiting. She gave him a big hug.

They drove along the beach road toward Grandma's cottage. The ocean sparkled in the sun, and lazy waves rolled onto the beach.

"Sam," Grandma said, "I have a surprise for you. There's a small harbor near our cottage, and I found out yesterday that swimming lessons are beginning there. Would you like to learn to swim?"

Sam was not absolutely sure, but he said, "Yes, Grandma."

It was a pleasant cottage facing the sea. They ate supper on the screened-in porch and because it had been a big day and Sam was tired, he went to bed early.

"Good night. Sweet dreams," Sam's grandmother said after he had said his prayers. He lay in bed. Home seemed far away.

"I know I'm going to like it here," he whispered to himself, "but will I be a good swimmer? Is it something hard to learn?"

The ocean's sound was a lullaby. He slept and dreamed he was wading in a creek back home.

Sam liked his swimming teacher. She was pretty and her voice was soft. "Call me Ruth," she told the class. There were five of them, and Sam was the smallest.

"Follow me," she said, and led them into the water. She showed them how to play as though they were swimming. Then she held them in deeper water, where they could kick and splash. It was fun.

By the end of the week, Ruth told them, "You can swim like ducks. Now it's time to try it by yourselves."

She stood waist-deep in the water. One by one, they swam out to her. Sam was last. He knew, he knew, he knew he could do it. With a deep breath he gave himself a push and swam toward her. What a wonderful feeling! All by himself he was sliding through the water and it was easy to stay on top.

"Good boy, Sam," Ruth said. "You are a winner." She gave each one in the class a blue ribbon to show how good he was.

"Sam," Grandma said, "Grandpa is going to be so proud when he comes out this weekend to take you fishing."

They met Sam's grandfather at the same bus stop where Grandma had picked up Sam. "Sam has something to show you," Grandmother said.

Sam took the blue ribbon out of his pocket. "A blue ribbon!" Grandpa said. "That means you're a winner." Grandmother told Grandpa Sam was a good swimmer.

Early next morning Sam and his grandfather put on life preservers and started out in the boat. Very quietly they went to a place Grandpa said was a good fishing spot.

Sam put his fishing line over the side of the boat and so did Grandfather. The fish began biting. One, two, three, four Sam caught.

Grandpa caught only two. "There are enough here for a good breakfast," Grandpa said. And they headed for home.

At the Seaside

When I was down beside the sea
A wooden spade they gave to me
    To dig the sandy shore.

My holes were empty like a cup.
In every hole the sea came up,
    Till it could come no more.

       Robert Louis Stevenson

A Sad Seaside Limerick

There once was a beach by the sea
As pleasant as pleasant could be
But after a bit,
    The litter bugs lit—
And now it's a sad sight to see.

A Trip to the Mountains

Sally's teenage cousin Ruth paid Sally's family a visit. When it was time for her to go home, she said, "Can Sally come with me? My family has moved to our cabin in Canada, and we can have lots of fun."

So Sally went with Ruth on the train. It went up through the hills and finally reached the little mountain town of Hightop.

Aunt Rose and Uncle Henry were glad to see Sally. They all got into their station wagon and drove toward the cabin. Sally had never seen a road with so many turns.

"We're driving through Pine Brook Forest," Uncle Henry told Sally. "If you keep your eyes open, you may see something strange."

Sure enough, when they rounded the next curve, there in the middle of the road was a big black bear. Uncle Henry stopped the car. "Roll up your windows. We want to be on the safe side," he said.

Sally held her breath. What would the bear do? Would he come over to the car? Uncle Henry honked the car's horn. Beep! Beep! Beep! The bear shook his head as if he didn't like the noise. Then he walked slowly off the road and into the nearby woods.

At breakfast on Sally's first morning in the cabin Ruth

said, "Today we are going to pick blueberries."

"What are blueberries?" Sally asked.

"They're very good to eat," said Uncle Henry.

"And very good when you bake them in a pie," said Aunt Rose. She gave Sally and Ruth tin pails to put the berries in.

"Watch out for animals," Uncle Henry warned. "They like to eat too."

The berry patch was close by, and Ruth showed Sally the bushes loaded with beautiful berries. Their pails were almost full when they heard a crashing sound.

"I think our bear is coming for some blueberries," Ruth said. "Let's hurry home."

When they were safely home, Sally helped take off the stems and wash the berries. Aunt Rose baked a pie. Yum-yum-yum! It was delicious.

One bright summer morning Ruth said, "Today we are going to explore." Sally was not quite sure what "explore" meant and she asked Ruth.

"We're going to a place to see what we can find," Ruth explained. "Back of the cabin there's a cave in the hillside. I've always wanted to have a look inside it."

Aunt Rose packed a picnic lunch for them. "Your father has already explored there and he says it is safe."

Uncle Henry gave each of them a flashlight. "Look at
the walls of the cave," he said. "You may see something
interesting."

Sally and Ruth ate their picnic lunch at the cave's en-
trance, which was like a big open door in the side of the
hill. When they had eaten the last of the cookies and finished the lemonade, Ruth said, "Now, let's explore."

The inside of the cave looked like a big room made
of rock. The light was dim, so they turned on their flash-

lights and inspected the walls. There were names written there and pictures, too, of animals and people.

"Maybe Indians lived here a long time ago," Ruth said, "and drew these pictures."

All at once they heard a fluttering above them. They shone their flashlights at the top of the walls. Funny little creatures were moving about up there and making noises.

"Oh! Oh!" Ruth exclaimed. "Those are bats, and I

don't think they want us to be here."

When they got home, Ruth told her parents what had happened. "It was exciting," Sally said. "I like to explore."

On the last day of Sally's visit, Uncle Henry said, "To-day we are going to climb to the top of Jolly Mountain."

He cut everyone a strong stick to help with climbing. Once again Aunt Rose packed picnic lunches. This time she made hot chocolate and poured it into a thermos bottle.

They started out. When Sally got tired, Uncle Henry

carried her on his back.

At last they reached the top of Jolly Mountain. "Whew!" Uncle Henry said. Then, while Aunt Rose and Uncle Henry put out food, Ruth and Sally picked some of the pretty yellow flowers that grew in the mountain meadow.

"Lunch is ready," Aunt Rose called. The long hike and the cool, clear air had given them good appetites.

"I feel like I'm on top of the world," Ruth said. She hugged Sally. "I'm glad you are here with me."

Visiting Canada had been great fun.

Cars, Taxis, and Other Wheels

There are big cars and small cars,
Fast cars and slow.
All of them take you
Where you want to go.

Taxi! Taxi! Hurry, please.
Take me to the train.
Take me to the circus.
Take me to a plane.
Take me to the zoo, and then,
Taxi! Take me home again.

Trains

Lots of fun to be a traveler
In a train upon a track.
It takes you where you want to go,
And then it takes you back.

76

Planes

The airport is a busy place
On the ground and in the air
For many, many kinds of planes
Are always landing there.

Buses

Buses go from town to town.
Some have a deck on top.
When buses see you waiting
Then they slow right down and stop.

Trucks

Trucks are busy as can be.

With many jobs to do.

Why don't you try and name some things

That trucks can bring for you?

The Happy Truck Driver's Song

I sing a song as I drive along
About the things I see.
My voice isn't good,
    but it's loud and strong,
And it keeps me company.

I wave a "hi" to cars passing by.
I look for signs of spring:
The grass is green, and high in the sky
Birds are on the wing.

As they munch their lunch,
    I shout to the cows.
I smile at the roadside flowers.
I wave to the farmer as he plows.
These are busy but happy hours.

So I sing a lot and the job I've got
Is one that I like, you know,
'Cause I'm never ever in just one spot,
I'm always on the go!

Learning What Signs Mean

These signs are made for you.
When you're going places,
They tell you what to do.

YIELD

STOP

BUS STOP

WAIT

ONE WAY

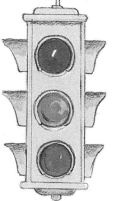

WALK

RAILROAD CROSSING

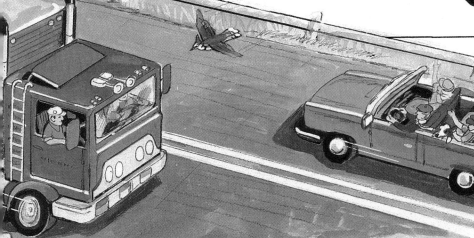

Let's Take a Make-Believe Trip

It is fun to pretend that you are going
    someplace.
Where will you go?
    To a lake? To a farm? To a big city?
    To an island? To the seashore?
    You name the place.
Now pack what you want to take.
    A shopping bag can be your
        suitcase.
    Put in some dress-up clothes.
    Do not forget a favorite toy.
    Will you want an apple to eat on the
        way—or a cookie?
How will you get there?
    Line up some chairs and pretend
        they are buses or trains or planes.
    Do you want to sit up front and
        drive?
    Or do you want to be a passenger?

Little Trips

A weekend walk with your mother and
father is fun.
There is so much to do for just everyone.
You can feed the birds with pieces of
bread,
Or go to the nearest park instead.
It is always great to take a ride
And have a look at the countryside.

Here are a few interesting places to visit:

- Your church. Your library.
- Where your mother or your father works.
- Your post office. You might mail a letter
  to someone you know.
- A greenhouse—especially when the
  weather is cold and wintry.
Where else would you like to go?

83

All About My Trip

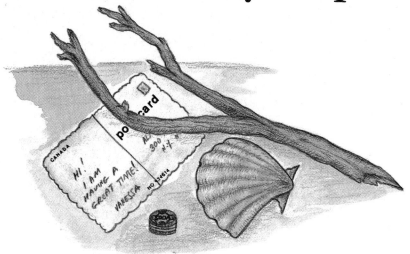

Part of the fun of taking a trip is telling a story about it when you come home. That way you can think about what you saw and what you did and you can do it over and over again.

While you are on the trip, here are some things you can do to help you remember what you see:

- Take along a notebook and draw some pictures of what you see.

- Have your mother or father take some snapshots of you while you are on the trip.

- Ask someone to help you make a list of what you see and do.

- Keep some things to remind you of the fun you had: ticket stubs, postcards, travel folders. Anything small you find along the way can be a good reminder.

When you are home again, you can make a scrapbook

of your trip. Your mother or father will help. Magazines may have pictures of things you saw. Cut them out and paste them on the pages of your trip notebook. Paste some of your trip reminders in your trip notebook or in a scrapbook. Tell your story to your mother and father. One of them can write it down for you.

NOTE TO PARENTS

Preparing for a trip can be rewarding. If there is time, write ahead for travel material. Share it with your children. If the trip is made in the family car, take along some things to help keep your children amused and interested. Empty paper towel rolls make fine telescopes for children. Be sure to include a couple of favorite toys and a familiar picture book or two. A tablet for drawing pictures and crayons can help pass the time. An old pocketbook can be filled with surprises, such as a magic slate, old Christmas cards, discarded costume jewelry, and long shoelaces with spools to string on them for necklaces.

Point out interesting things along the road. With older children, you can play alphabet games: "Now we are looking for things that start with A."

Remember to take along a thermos and snacks!

When Robert Louis Stevenson, the poet, was growing up, he was often ill and spent much time in bed. He could not run and play, and often entertained himself with make believe. Probably, he thought of his shadow as a very close friend. Here is a poem he wrote about it.

from My Shadow

I have a little shadow that
    Goes in and out with me,
And what can be the use of him
    Is more than I can see.

He is very, very like me
    From the heels up to the head;
And I see him jump before me,
    When I jump into my bed.

The funniest thing about him
    Is the way he likes to grow—
Not at all like proper children,
    Which is always very slow;

For he sometimes shoots up taller
    Like a bouncing rubber ball,
And he sometimes gets so little
    That there's none of him at all.

He hasn't got a notion of
    How children ought to play,
And can only make a fool of me
    In every sort of way.

One morning, very early,
    Before the sun was up,
I rose and found the shining dew
    On every buttercup;

But my lazy little shadow,
    Like a little sleepyhead,
Had stayed at home behind me
    And was fast asleep in bed.

Robert Louis Stevenson

Shadow Talk

I'm your little shadow
So be careful, can't you see—
Any trouble you get into
Is trouble, too, for me!

So, listen to your shadow:

Don't leave your toys on the floor
'Cause you might trip and go
    kerplunk!
And you and even I, what's more,
Could get an awful bump.

Your shadow says:

Anytime we climb the stair,
Climb with care! Climb with care!
And this is something else I've
    found—
Go slowly when we're coming down!

Your shadow reminds you:

I know that you know that this is
    very true—
You mustn't talk to strangers
When they try to talk to you.
And if a stranger offers you
Some candy, or a ride,
Just hurry home and tell your folks
When you are safe inside.
And never leave your friends and go
With anyone you do not know!

Some Do's to Do

I get so tired of *"Don't!"*
Don't you?
So here's a special list
Of *"Do!"*

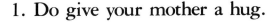

1. Do give your mother a hug.
2. Do give your father a hug.
3. Do say "hello" to the folks you know.
4. Do wash your hands before meals.
5. Do learn to say "I'm sorry" when you make a mistake.
6. Do something nice for someone.
7. Do help your mother.
8. Do help your father.
9. Do be nice to all your friends and family.
10. Do try to be good.
11. Do wave goodby when someone leaves.
12. Do remember to say your prayers at night.

Mr. Do Right

Do you know what "do right" means? "Do right" often seems to be a small voice that whispers to you. It tells you the right thing to do. It helps you to remember what you should do. It warns you when you are about to make a mistake. Here's make-believe talk between you and Mr. Do Right.

You: (early in the morning) I think I'll skip brushing my teeth this morning.

Mr. Do Right: Brush them! Good health habits are more fun than toothaches.

You: (at breakfast) I don't want my oatmeal. I don't want to drink my milk. I'm going to eat cookies for breakfast.

Mr. Do Right: Eat the things you should. You want to grow up strong and healthy, don't you?

You: (at play) If I cannot be first, I won't play.

Mr. Do Right: Think of others. What if everyone acted like that!

You: (playing outside) Oh, look at those pretty flowers in the yard next door. I'm going to pick some.

Mr. Do Right: Wait! Remember you must ask first. They don't belong to you.

You: I'm angry because I can't play in the rain. I'm going to slam the door as hard as I can!

Mr. Do Right: That will just make you look silly.

You: (at bath time) I'm going to see how big a splash I can make.

Mr. Do Right: And make a big mess for your mother to clean up. Now you don't really want to do that.

You: It's bedtime and I'm going to bed nicely without saying I want to stay up a while longer.

Mr. Do Right: I'm proud of you. You are really growing up.

Surprise!

"I know a secret," said Jennifer one day in March. She was talking with her friend Sally, who lived next door.

"What is it? What is it?" Sally asked.

"Can't tell. Can't tell," Jennifer said. She ran back to her house. Once inside she went to her room and got the envelope that had come for her in the morning mail. She took it to her mother.

"Read it to me again, please," Jennifer asked. Her mother took the invitation out of the envelope. There was a picture of a big birthday cake on it with candles burning brightly.

And there was a message:

DEAR JENNIFER,
PLEASE COME to
A SECRET SURPRISE
birthdAY PARTY
FOR YOUR FRIENd, SALLY.
WhEN: 2:30 iN thE
AFTERNOON ON thE
FOURth dAY OF MARCH
WHERE: AT MY HOUSE
Linda

"Put on your thinking cap," Jennifer's mother said, "and think of a nice birthday present for Sally."

Jennifer thought hard, but as hard as she tried, she could think only of things that she would have liked herself.

"Maybe if we go to the toy store, we'll see something Sally will like," Jennifer's mother said. The trip to the store was a big success. They came home with a suitcase for Sally's doll clothes.

Jennifer helped her mother wrap Sally's present, and her mother helped Jennifer sign her name to the birthday card for Sally.

The day of the party was bright, sunny, and windy. Just the kind of day one expects in March. "Maybe you should have bought a kite for Sally," Jennifer's father joked. "It's a great day for kite flying."

When Jennifer got to Linda's house, there was her friend Sam and other boys and girls.

"Sally's coming over later to look at my new cassette," said Linda. "She doesn't know that I know today is her birthday."

They put all of Sally's birthday presents on a big table in the center of the living room. Then they hung balloons of many colors all about the room. Finally, when everything was ready, they each chose

a hiding place. Linda was looking out the window.

"Here she comes," she called out. "Everybody hide!"
They ran to their hiding places.

Linda's mother met Sally at the door. "Linda's waiting
for you in the living room," she said.

When Sally reached the doorway, all the children
jumped out from their hiding places. "Surprise! Surprise!"
they called. Sally was truly surprised.

"Open your presents, Sally," they said. As Sally opened
each one, everyone oohed and ahed.

Sally thanked each friend as she opened the presents. When Sally opened the doll suitcase and thanked Jennifer for it, she said, "Erma Sue and Mary Lou thank you, too."

Then Linda's mother lined up two rows of chairs and they played musical chairs to the tune of "Happy Birthday to You." And Sally, the birthday girl, won.

At the right time, the curtains were pulled in the living room, and it became very dim. In came the birthday cake with candles brightly shining. It looked like the cake on Jennifer's card to Sally. There was ice cream, too. It was a great surprise party!

This poem was written many, many years ago and may have been read to your grandmother and grandfather by their parents. It is still something to think about today.

I Love You, Mother

"I love you, Mother," said little John;
Then, forgetting his work, his cap went on,
And he was off to the garden swing,
Leaving his mother the wood to bring.

"I love you, Mother," said little Nell,
"I love you more than tongue can tell."
Then she teased and pouted half the day
Till her mother rejoiced when she went to play.

"I love you, Mother," said little Fan.
"Today I'll help you all I can."
To the cradle then she did softly creep,
And rocked the baby till it fell asleep.

"I love you, Mother," again they said,
Three little children going to bed.
How do you think the mother guessed,
Which of them really loved her best?

Joy Allison

Things to Remember

Early to bed
And early to rise
Makes a man healthy, wealthy, and wise.

Benjamin Franklin

Stand tall! Sit straight!
And then you will look and feel
JUST GREAT!

To look your very, very best
These *helpers* can't be beat—
One of them you know as "Clean."
The other one is "Neat."

When at Table

Take little bites
Whatever you do,
And then remember
To chew, chew, CHEW!

First Aid

Small cuts and scratches
Are not a big deal,
But keep them clean
So they will heal.

Things to Learn

What is hot can burn.
What is sharp can hurt,
Nasty germs like dirt.
Exercise
Is wise.
When it is cold,
Wear a wrap.
When you are tired,
Take a nap.
And, when all is said and done,
Have fun,
Have fun,
HAVE FUN!

A Promise Is a Promise

Sam's next-door neighbor, Mrs. Morris, stopped by with her dog Fluffy to see Sam and his mother.

"I have a favor to ask you, Sam," she said. "Can you take care of Fluffy for a week? Mr. Morris and I are flying out West to stay at a ranch. We hate to put Fluffy in a kennel. She usually gets sick."

"Oh, Mother, may I?" Sam asked.

"It will be lots of work, Sam," his mother answered.

"I promise. I promise," Sam said. "I'll take good care of Fluffy."

So it was agreed that Fluffy would stay at Sam's house for a week. When Mrs. Morris brought the little dog over, she also brought Fluffy's bed, her dishes, and her special dog food.

Mrs. Morris said, "She must be walked early morning and late afternoon and fed right after she walks. Will you remember that, Sam?"

"I promise," Sam said. The first day Sam had fun walking and feeding Fluffy. When his mother awakened him on the second morning, Sam was very sleepy. "Please, Mom, you walk her," he said.

"You promised!" his mother reminded him. So Sam took Fluffy for a walk.

The third day Sam's friend Benny appeared at Sam's front door.

"Hi," he said. "We're going to the seashore for the rest of the week. Mom and Dad said I could bring Sam along!"

"Boy! Oh, boy!" Sam exclaimed. He looked at his mother. "Please, may I go?"

"What about Fluffy?" his mother asked.

"Why can't you and Dad take care of her?" said Sam.

"You promised Mrs. Morris that you would, Sam," his mother said. *"A promise is a promise."*

"It's not fair," Sam said, but he knew his mother was right. Benny turned away sadly.

Sam took good care of Fluffy. He even talked to her.

"We've both got to make the best of it," he told her.

Fluffy was very happy when Mrs. Morris finally came for her.

"You certainly kept your promise, Sam," Mrs. Morris said. "Fluffy looks wonderful." She handed Sam a package.

"It's a present," she said.

Sam opened it. It was a cowboy suit!

"May I try it on?" he asked. His mom nodded, and Sam went to his room.

When he came back, he was Cowboy Sam. The suit fitted perfectly.

"Here's a cowboy hat to go with it," Mrs. Morris said.

Sam let out a whoop.

"Wait 'till Benny sees this. Thank you, Mrs. Morris."

After Mrs. Morris left, Sam's mother asked, "Was keeping your promise worth it?"

Cowboy Sam smiled. "Next time," he said, "I'm not going to make such quick promises!"

Little Boy Lost

A new family moved in on the same street where Sally and Sam lived. Sally and Sam watched as the moving men unloaded the big van. They were hoping the new people had some children.

Sure enough, the moving men finally unloaded a tricycle and a small wagon.

"We'll have a new friend," Sally said.

The next day they saw the new boy riding his tricycle up and down the driveway. He was young, maybe three years old. While Sally and Sam were watching, he turned his tricycle too quickly and it turned over. "Oh, my!" Sam said. He and Sally ran over to help the little boy.

"Fell down," the little boy said. He smiled. "Not hurt."

"Good!" said Sally. "My name is Sally, and this is Sam. What's your name?"

"Tommy," the little boy told them.

Tommy had an older sister, Donna. Sally and Sam soon met her. It was summertime, and all the boys and girls in the

neighborhood had good times playing together. Early one evening, they were playing in Sally's yard.

"Let's play hide and seek," Donna said. "Tommy loves the game. I'll be *it*. Everyone run and hide."

"Me hide," Tommy said, and he followed the others.

"Ready or not, here I come," Donna called out.

The boys and girls started racing in. Donna caught some; others came in free. At last everyone was in except Tommy.

"Come on, Tommy," Donna called. "You get in free."

Tommy did not answer. They all called. Still there was no answer. Donna looked worried.

"Let's all look for him," she said. "I'm afraid he's lost!"

While the girls and boys started searching, Donna ran home to tell her parents that Tommy was lost.

Soon it would be dark. Other parents joined in the search. Now and then everyone would stop calling and listen very carefully, hoping to hear Tommy, but there was only silence.

"Don't you think we should phone the police?" Tommy's worried mother asked.

"Yes," Tommy's father answered, and he left to call.

Suddenly, Donna called out, "There's Tommy now!" She pointed down the street. An old lady was leading Tommy toward the searchers. His face was stained with tears. With a happy cry he ran to his mother.

"Me got lost," Tommy said.

"I heard him on my porch," the old lady said. "He couldn't tell me his last name or where he lived. Finally, I heard all the shouting so we headed this way."

Everyone thanked her.

They were so happy to see Tommy again, safe and sound and ready to go home.

"Tommy! Tommy!" His mother hugged him. "When we get home we're going to practice your last name and your address."

"Me learn," Tommy said.

And he did! Tommy was never lost again.

NOTE TO PARENTS

Babies are born caring only about their own comfort. How to eat properly, care for others, and practice basic rules of health are things that must be taught along with basic values.

Parents are the first teachers. Most rules have good reasons behind them. Explaining both the rules and the reasons is an important job. In this sense, the home is really the child's first schoolroom.

This section provides some of the many important things boys and girls must learn as they grow up. A child's name and address are vital pieces of information. As early as possible, these facts should be taught. Certain things, like warnings about strangers, cannot be sugarcoated; however, they can be discussed without instilling fear and alarm in your children.

Your responsibility is great. The reward of knowing your children have been thoughtfully and carefully informed is even greater.

Let's Play

Let's play we are fire trucks
  Racing down the street.
Let's play we are horses
  With hay and oats to eat.
Let's play we are fishes
  Swimming in a pool.
Let's play we are astronauts.
  Let's play we're in school.
Let's play we are circus clowns,
  Or actors on TV.
To play a game of let's pretend
  Is fun for you and me!

Good Friends

Sunny days and rainy days—
Any kind of weather—
Are always just the best of days
When good friends play together.

Be Good to Me

I don't want to play in your yard.
I don't like you anymore.
You'll be sorry when you see me
Sliding down our cellar door.

You can't holler down our rain barrel.
You can't climb our apple tree.
Oh, I don't want to play in your yard,
If you won't be good to me.

Making Up

That friends like us sometimes may fuss
Is very sad but true,
But making up can be quite nice,
And that we always do!

Caring and Sharing

Jennifer lived next door to Sally. She was younger than Sally. They often played that Sally was her mother and that she was Sally's little girl. One morning, when Sally was in the yard, Jennifer came running over.

"Look," she said to Sally, "I won a prize." She held out a box of crayons.

"They're pretty," Sally said. "What was the prize for?"

"My mom gave it to me for brushing my teeth after every meal for a whole week without being told to," Jennifer said. "Now I can do a lot of coloring."

"I hope you'll share your prize," remarked Sally, who loved to color.

"What's sharing?" Jennifer asked.

"It's letting other kids have a turn with your toys, or letting them color with your crayons," Sally told her.

"I'm going to show Linda my new crayons," Jennifer said.

Linda was an older girl. She had just started school.

"How nice," Linda said, when she saw Jennifer's prize. "I have a new crayon sharpener."

"How nice," Jennifer echoed.

Linda looked at the crayons. "Let's sharpen them with my new crayon sharpener," she suggested.

"Is that sharing?" Jennifer asked.

Linda did not answer. She got a plastic jar and started sharpening Jennifer's new crayons. Little colored shavings from each crayon fell in the plastic jar. There were red shavings, yellow shavings, blue, green, and orange shavings. "How pretty!" Linda exclaimed. "Let's do some more."

Linda sharpened Jennifer's crayons some more while Jennifer watched. The crayons became shorter and shorter. At last the jar was filled to the top. But now there was nothing left of Jennifer's crayons to color with.

It was then that Sally came over to see what was going on. Jennifer started to cry.

"I was sharing," said Jennifer between sobs. "Now I can't color with my crayons."

"That's the wrong kind of sharing," Sally said to Jennifer. "Don't cry."

She whispered something to Linda. "Wait right here," Sally told Jennifer. She and Linda ran to their homes. When they came back, they brought crayons and three coloring books.

"These are for you," Sally and Linda told Jennifer. They each gave Jennifer some of their crayons. Then Sally handed Jennifer a coloring book. The three girls sat down in the grass and started to color.

"I like this kind of sharing," Jennifer said.

"It's the best kind," Sally told her.

"May I borrow your blue?" Linda asked Sally, as they continued to color their pretty pictures.

"I really do have mighty fine friends," said Jennifer.

Games with Friends

Clap the Song Game

This is a rhythm game for two or more. The one who is *it* thinks of the name of a song, for example, "Happy Birthday to You," or "Jingle Bells." The other players try to guess the song. Instead of singing the words, though, the one who is *it* claps the song—one clap for each syllable, pausing between words. The person who guesses the song is then *it*.

Musical Chairs

This is an indoor game for any number of players. If there are nine players, for example, line up two rows of four chairs each. The music begins and the players march around the chairs.

Without warning, the music stops. Each player sits down in the nearest chair. One player, of course, is left without a chair and must leave the game. One chair is removed, and the game continues.

At last there are only two players and one chair. The one who manages to sit in it when the music stops wins the game.

Statues

A favorite children's game is statues. The player who is *it* takes the hand of a friend. They whirl around together until the person who is *it* suddenly lets go.

The second player then becomes a statue in the exact position he or she was in at the end of the spin. When all the players have had their whirl, the leader selects the best or funniest statue, and that player is then *it*.

Some other games that are fun: Drop the Handkerchief, Hide and Seek, Lemonade, Wood Tag, Beanbag, Blindman's Bluff, and Pin the Tail on the Donkey.

Playground Fun

Playgrounds and parks are for everyone. When you and your friends are playing, you should remember safety rules. Getting hurt or hurting someone else is not fun. Here are some do's and don'ts to help you have more playground fun.

1. Do not play near swings when they are being used.

2. Do swing one person at a time. Do not swing too high. Wait until the swing has stopped before you get off.

3. Do go down a slide feet first. Keep your hands away from the sides. Wait until the slider ahead of you has stepped away from the bottom before you start down.

4. Do not push. Do not shove. Be polite.

5. Do not get off a seesaw without warning the person at the other end.

6. Do keep your playground clean.

7. Do not fly a kite near electric wires or wires of any kind.

8. Do not play in the street.

9. Do not carry a passenger on your bicycle.

120

121

Nursery School Time

Teddy's mother was getting him ready for his first day at nursery school. "You'll meet new friends at the nursery school," she said.

"I don't want any new friends," Teddy said.

Teddy did not say a word as they drove to the nursery school.

"Here we are," Teddy's mother said as they stopped in front of a big house. There was a fence around it, and over the gate was a sign: HAPPY TIME NURSERY SCHOOL.

A very pretty lady met them. Teddy remembered her. She had once come to his house and they had talked about the nursery school.

"Good morning, Teddy," she said. "Don't you want to meet some new friends?" Teddy did not say anything.

"This is Angelica," Miss Hampel said, "and here are Nicholas, Becky, and Charles." Teddy held on to his mother's hand.

Nicholas smiled and held out his hand to Teddy. He led Teddy to a corner of the room, where there were shelves filled with toys. Teddy had never seen so many.

Nicholas took a fire truck, and Teddy picked out a police car. They raced with them. Sometimes the fire truck won and sometimes the police car won.

Teddy liked Nicholas. When Teddy looked around he saw that his mother had left, but it did not matter. Teddy was having fun.

After a while Miss Hampel said, "Teddy, you and Nicholas can sit here." She gave each child a big sheet of paper and crayons.

"We're going to draw pictures," Miss Hampel told them. "Anything you want to draw—the toy you were playing with, an apple, a flower, a balloon, or just something you make up."

After they drew their pictures and showed them to one another, Miss Hampel told them a story.

When Teddy's mother came to pick him up, he could not believe it was time to leave. The morning had gone so fast. Teddy brought Nicholas over to his mother.

"This is Nicholas," he said. "He's my new friend."

Teddy's mother smiled. "Some day you must come home and have lunch with us," she told Nicholas. "I'll ask your mother."

On the way home, Teddy said to his mother, "I like nursery school. May I go back tomorrow?" His mother nodded. "And may Nicholas come home with us?"

"Very soon," his mother said to Nicholas. "I promise."

Manners

Politeness

Hearts like doors, will open with ease
To very, very little keys,
And don't forget that two of these
Are "Thank you, Sir," and "If you please."

What a Shame!

Little Polly Hammers wouldn't mind her manners.

Truly awful Tommy Snell would stamp his feet and
     sometimes yell.

And there, of course, was Betty Bemper
    who nearly always lost her temper,

Not to mention Billy Blair who never ever would play fair.

It really was a downright shame—

'Cause when they had a party,

Absolutely no one came! Not even Marty Smarty.

The Goops

The Goops they lick their fingers,
    And the Goops they lick their
      knives;

They spill their broth on the tablecloth—
    Oh, they lead disgusting lives!

The Goops they talk while eating,
    And loud and fast they chew;

And that is why I'm glad that I
    Am not a Goop—are you?

Gelett Burgess

Kind Words

Kind words are just like presents,
    And this you can believe.
They really are much nicer
    To give than to receive.

Having Friends

Having friends is very special.
    Having friends is very nice.
But to have a friend, you must be a
        friend,
    And here is some advice.

Share your toys and share your joys.
    And other things to learn:
Don't always say, "I want my way!"
    Be patient. Wait your turn.

Nobody likes a whiner,
    And no one likes a tease.
Good sports and happy smilers,
    Are always sure to please.

The best rule to remember

    Is the golden one, it's true:

Just always do to others

    As you wish they'd do to you.

Some Be Nice Rules

1. Be nice to your baby-sitter.
2. Go to bed when it is bedtime.
3. Ask politely. Do not beg.
4. Be helpful.
5. Show how many things you can do for yourself.
6. Do not always demand to watch your favorite television program.

Can you think of some other Be Nice rules?

NOTE TO PARENTS

Playtime should always be fun time, but learning to play with others and learning unselfishness is important and serious business. Caring and sharing cannot be overemphasized.

Park and playground activities for the young child should always be supervised.

Sally's Kitten

After Sally and her parents had their supper, the November evening turned much colder.

"I'm going to close the garage door," Sally's father said.

He came back in a few minutes. "We have a visitor in the garage. I can hear it, but I can't find it."

Sally and her parents hurried to the garage to look and listen.

"There!" Sally whispered. "I hear it." Her mother and father nodded. They heard it, too. But where was the sound coming from? Sally looked under the car. There was nothing there.

"Meow," the hoarse, small sound came again, like a cry for help.

At last Sally found the kitten behind the clothes dryer. Crouching there, it looked frightened and hungry. "Poor little kitty," Sally said. "It's orange," she told her parents.

"I'll warm some milk," her mother said.

When Sally's mother came back, she

130

placed the saucer of milk on the floor beside
the clothes dryer. "It's so thin," Sally's mother
said.

The kitten began to lap up the milk.
Then Sally's father petted it—oh, so gently
—and picked it up carefully and placed it

in an old blanket. The kitten sniffed the blanket and then
curled up until it looked like a little orange ball. "I'll sing
you to sleep," Sally told the kitten. And she sang.

Good night. Good night.

Pretty kitty.

Sleep tight. Sleep tight.

Pretty kitty.

When Sally and her parents were upstairs, Sally's first
words were, "May I keep it?"

"It may belong to someone else," her father answered.
"Let's wait and see."

No one came looking for it though.

They kept giving it milk but it still seemed very weak.

"We must take it to the animal doctor. He can check to see how healthy it is and give it medicine," Sally's father said.

The animal doctor looked at the small kitten. "This cat has not had a good home," he told them. He smiled at Sally. "I'll keep it here for a few days and try to make it well. If it was smart enough to find its way to your house, I think it will try hard to get well."

Back home Sally thought of names for the kitten. She remembered that the animal doctor had said it was a smart cat.

"I'm going to name it Smarty," Sally told her mother. Waiting for Smarty to get well seemed forever. Each day Sally's mother called the doctor.

"Not yet," he said. Then one day he told them the kitten was well.

Oh, the kitten looked so much better. When they were home, it snuggled close to Sally.

"Oh, Smarty, I love you," Sally said. Smarty yawned.

"I'm going to sing you to sleep again," Sally said.

Good night. Good night.

Little Smarty.

Sleep tight. Sleep tight.

Little Smarty.

The kitten was asleep in Sally's lap. And Sally was a very happy girl who now had a very healthy pet.

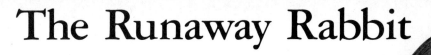

The Runaway Rabbit

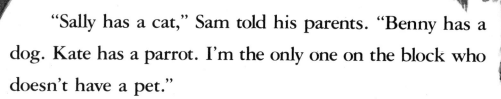

"Sally has a cat," Sam told his parents. "Benny has a dog. Kate has a parrot. I'm the only one on the block who doesn't have a pet."

"When you visit your grandmother, you can always play with her tabby cat," Sam's mother said.

"It isn't the same," Sam replied.

"We've never had pets," said his father.

"It isn't fair," said Sam.

"I guess we could start having pets," his mother said.

"What kind?" Sam asked.

"Something quiet," she said.

"Something that doesn't scratch furniture," his father said.

They decided the best idea was to go to the nearby pet store and look for a pet.

Mrs. Harris, the lady at the pet store, showed them

guinea pigs, goldfish, and gerbils. They were nice but not for Sam.

Mrs. Harris showed them monkeys, macaws, and mice. Sam's parents said, "No thank you," and Sam agreed.

Then Mrs. Harris led them to the rabbits. There were gray rabbits, black rabbits, and spotted rabbits. But the rabbit Sam liked best was a big, white rabbit with long whiskers and a pink nose. His fur was soft and silky.

"I like him," Sam said.

"We'll take him," his father said, and his mother bought a book called *The Care and Feeding of Rabbits*.

135

Sam named the rabbit Softie. Sam's father built a rabbit house for Softie. The weather was warm, so they put the house outdoors under an apple tree.

Softie liked his new home. Several times a day Sam would take Softie out of his rabbit house. Sam would pet him and Softie would nibble the green grass.

There was a problem! If Sam left Softie alone, even for a minute, he hopped away to the neighbor's garden.

One day, Sam found him nibbling a cabbage leaf. Oh, my!

Another day, Softie hopped over to Sally's yard. When Sam found him, Sally's cat Smarty and Softie were staring at each other.

"Come home, Softie," Sam said. "I don't think cats like rabbits."

The next time Softie ran away, Sam couldn't find him. He called to his mother to help look.

Where had that rabbit gone?

They heard Benny's dog barking. Before they got to Benny's house, Softie appeared, taking big, fast hops. Benny's dog was chasing him, and Softie didn't like all that barking.

"Softie, Softie," Sam said, as he picked him up. "You must stop running away."

Sam's mother bought a little collar and a leash for Softie. When Softie was in the yard, he would wear his collar. Sam would hold the leash fastened to it. After that, Softie never ran away.

Sam and Softie played together every day for a long time.

The Pet Show

Sally's kitten won a ribbon for having the loudest purr.

And Sam's rabbit won first prize for his silky fur.

Hannah's hamster was a winner for best exercise.

Oliver's owl was called smartest for simply looking wise.

For loudest bark, Benny's pup was said to be the best.
George's goldfish won first prize in the swimming test.

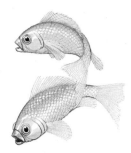

Kate's parrot screeched, "I want a cracker,"
And Willie's duck was judged best quacker.

Every pet made lots of noise,
    And when the show was through,
Everyone said they never had heard
    Such a hullabaloo!

 meow

 squeak

 bow-wow

 whirr

 yak

quack

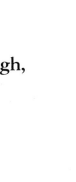

 hoot

splish-splash

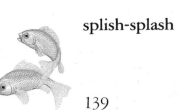

139

Happy Pets

Happy, healthy pets must have the right kind of food, a proper place to live, and plenty of exercise.

Food: Be careful not to overfeed your pet. If it leaves food in its dish, give it less next time. It is better to feed too little than too much. Clean dishes are a *must*. So is fresh water, which should always be in the same place and present all of the time. If possible, your pet should be fed at the same times daily.

Home: Indoor pets should have comfortable, warm beds, frequently cleaned. Outdoor pets should be given shelters that protect them from rain and cold.

Exercise: Large pets need more exercise than small ones. Cats provide their own exercise. Walking a dog is a happy time for both of you. Many places require by law that the dog be on a leash. It is always the wise thing to do.

Here are some other things to remember:

Tell your pet often how good it is.
Speak gently and do not tease.
Use short words, such as sit, lie, stay, come, and no.
Dogs and cats need careful brushing every day.
Give your pet a name and use it.
Pets get tired just as you do. Let them have plenty of rest.
If your pet is ill, be sure to call an animal doctor.
Enjoy your pet, and give it love!

Pet Poems

You can see a cat's whiskers.
You can see a cat's fur.
You can see its tail twitching,
But you can't see its purr!

I had a little pony.
His coat was colored gray.
At breakfast time I fed him oats.
For supper he had hay.

Hark, hark, the little dog barks.
What does he want to say?
"Thank you for my tasty meal.
Now, please, come out and play!"

Some people think that mice are nice.
There is nothing wrong with that.
But if you're having mice as pets,
You shouldn't keep a cat.

There once was a turtle named Myrtle—
A pleasant, but most silent pet.
She stayed in her shell, and lived very well—
Best of all when the weather was wet.

Goldfish swimming in your bowl
You keep so very busy,
But when you swim in circles,
Don't you get a little dizzy?

NOTE TO PARENTS

The decision whether or not to have a pet should be a parental one. Both you and the pet will be happier if you carefully consider space requirements and provide yourself with as much knowledge as possible about the pet's living habits and physical needs before the final selection is made. Training the pet and teaching children how to care for the pet are factors of equal importance. The joy of having a healthy pet is great, and so are the responsibilities.

Signs and Sounds of Winter

Frost is on the windowpane.
Mitten time is here.
The days are getting shorter.
Could Christmas Day be near?

Boys and girls slide down the hill.
Skaters on the ice.
Mr. Snowman seems to say,
"Wintertime is nice!"

Fireplace logs are burning bright.
Hear the sleighbells jingle.
Don't forget to feed the birds
Or write to old Kris Kringle.

A Visit from St. Nicholas

by Clement C. Moore

'Twas the night before Christmas, when all through
    the house
Not a creature was stirring, not even a mouse;
The stockings were hung by the chimney with care,
In hopes that St. Nicholas soon would be there;

The children were nestled all snug in their beds,
While visions of sugarplums danced through their heads;
And Mamma in her 'kerchief, and I in my cap,
Had just settled our brains for a long winter's nap,—

When out on the lawn there arose such a clatter,
I sprang from my bed to see what was the matter;
Away to the window I flew like a flash,
Tore open the shutters and threw up the sash.

The moon on the breast of the new-fallen snow
Gave the luster of midday to objects below;
When, what to my wondering eyes should appear,
But a miniature sleigh, and eight tiny reindeer,

With a little old driver, so lively and quick,

I knew in a moment it must be Saint Nick.

More rapid than eagles his coursers they came,

And he whistled, and shouted, and called them by name:

"Now, Dasher! now, Dancer! now, Prancer and Vixen!

On, Comet! on, Cupid! on, Donder and Blitzen!

To the top of the porch! to the top of the wall!

Now, dash away! dash away! dash away all!"

As dry leaves that before the wild hurricane fly,

When they meet with an obstacle, mount to the sky,

So up to the housetop the coursers they flew,

With the sleigh full of toys—and St. Nicholas too!

And then, in a twinkling, I heard on the roof,

The prancing and pawing of each little hoof.

As I drew in my head, and was turning around,

Down the chimney St. Nicholas came with a bound.

He was dressed all in fur, from his head to his foot,

And his clothes were all tarnished with ashes and soot!

A bundle of toys he had flung on his back,

And he looked like a peddler just opening his pack.

His eyes—how they twinkled! his dimples, how merry!

His cheeks were like roses, his nose like a cherry!

His droll little mouth was drawn up like a bow,

And the beard on his chin was as white as the snow . . .

The stump of a pipe he held tight in his teeth,

And the smoke, it encircled his head like a wreath;

He had a broad face, and a little round belly,

That shook, when he laughed, like a bowlful of jelly.

He was chubby and plump, a right jolly old elf,

And I laughed, when I saw him, in spite of myself.

A wink of his eye, and a twist of his head,

Soon gave me to know I had nothing to dread.

He spoke not a word, but went straight to his work,

And filled all the stockings—then turned with a jerk,

And laying his finger aside of his nose,

And giving a nod, up the chimney he rose.

He sprang to his sleigh, to his team gave a whistle,

And away they all flew, like the down of a thistle.

But I heard him exclaim, ere he drove out of sight,

"Happy Christmas to all! and to all a good night!"

Snow Fun

Many people have never seen snow because it does not fall in all parts of the world. Where it does fall though, almost everyone agrees that playing in the snow is fun. Of course, it is important to dress warmly for snow play, and it is equally important not to play outside too long on a very cold day.

Build a Snow Man: **One very large ball of snow is the lower part. A smaller ball of snow is his middle. The smallest ball of snow is his head. Eyes can be pieces of coal or small rocks. A carrot makes a fine nose. You can shape his mouth in a wide grin. A piece of red Christmas ribbon or yarn makes his grin even friendlier. Dress him up with old clothes.**

Other Ways to Have Fun: **Build a snow fort or Eskimo igloo with big blocks of snow. Sleds and snow go together, but remember your safety rules. Each snowflake is shaped differently. Catch some on dark paper. Look quickly through a magnifying glass before they melt.**

Valentine's Day

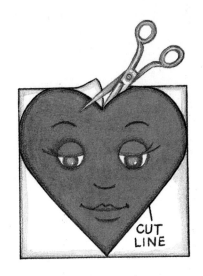

Valentine's Day is a favorite winter holiday. February 14th is the date. It is a day to tell people how much you like them. One way to tell them is to send valentines. You can make them in the shape of a heart.

Think of people you would like to give valentines: Mother, Dad, Brother, Sister, Grandmother, Grandfather, friends. Can you think of others?

You can make a valentine person, too. A big heart turned upside down is the body. A smaller heart is the face. Draw eyes, nose, and mouth on the face. Smaller hearts can be ears. Paste them all together. Give your valentine person a name.

A Valentine Tongue Twister

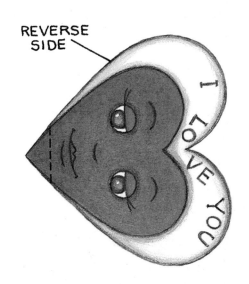

Violet's violin valentine vanished from the village van. Visitor Vern
on vacation from Vine View Valley
found Violet's violin valentine
again.

Signs and Sounds of Spring

Winds of March,
And April showers,
Green grass, new leaves,
And May's bright flowers.

Kites flying high—
Birds building a nest.
Chipmunks wake up
From their winter rest.

A gift for Mother
On her day.
Baseball begins—
It's time to play!

For Arbor Day
You plant a tree.
Oh, spring is grand
For you and me!

Sam and His Special Kite

"Sam," his father said, "our town is going to have a kite day. There will be prizes for the kite that flies highest, the prettiest kite, and the most special kite."

"Let's make a kite that is special," Sam said.

So Sam and his father got a book about kites at the library. They had no idea there were so many different kites. The kite Sam liked best was one that whistled when it

151

flew through the air, so they decided to make a whistle kite.

It was a simple two-stick kite. What made it special were the whistles. Both Sam and his father knew that kites must never have any metal parts. Metal would make them dangerous because it could attract lightning.

So they found a bamboo fishing pole for making the whistles. They cut it up into very small pieces. Then Sam's father made little notches at different places in the small bamboo whistles. They fastened the whistles all around the kite.

"Time to see if it works," Sam's father said.

The day was clear and windy. They went to the big hill where the kites would be flown. Down the hill Sam ran, holding the kite string. His father held the kite up until a gust of wind lifted it. Up, up, up it sailed, higher and higher. Sam and his father listened.

And then they heard a merry tune. The kite was whistling. It worked!

Kite day was a perfect spring day. Sam and his parents hurried to the big hill. Many boys and girls were there with their kites.

What a sight! Big kites, tiny kites, flag kites, even dragon kites!

Guess who won the prize for most special kite? You are right. It was Sam with his kite that whistled a merry tune!

Kite, kite. All right.
Fly by day. Not by night.

Rainy Day Fun

Start an indoor sweet potato vine: Put a sweet potato in a jar, one half in water, the other out of water. Place it in a warm, dark place. When roots and stems appear, place it in sunlight. Now watch it grow.

POTATO PLANT

Three More Rainy Day Things to Do:

Have a Cook-in.

Help mother bake cookies or make candy. Be very careful not to touch the stove or hot cookie sheet.

COOKIES

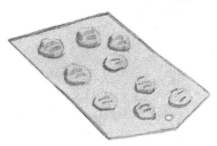

Make Your Own Puzzle.

Paste a picture from an old magazine on cardboard. Cut it up into pieces of different sizes. Mix them up and then fit them back together.

PUZZLE

Make a Play Tent.

A sheet or blanket draped over a card table or two chairs makes a play tent. You can pretend you are an Indian or a desert chief or a camper inside your tent.

May Day Queen

All the neighbors agreed it would be fun to have a May Day party.

"We'll put up a tall Maypole with colored ribbon streamers," Sally's mother said.

The children decided they would choose a May Day queen. When the votes were counted, Sally won! They made her a crown. Then Sally gave the signal to start circling the Maypole. When all the ribbons were wrapped around the Maypole, the picnic began.

It was a great May Day, and Sally was queen.

Signs and Sounds of Summer

Summertime is happy time.
Roses bloom in June.
Time to cut the grass again.
Picnic treats at noon.

Fireworks light the sky at night,
Insects hum and sing.
August days are lazy days.
Birds are on the wing.

Fun to splash in swimming pools.
Watch the busy bee.
Ice-cream cones are oh, so good!
Just for you and me.

Canada Day

On the first day of July, Canadians celebrate one of their country's most important holidays. Originally called Dominion Day, it is now known as Canada Day.

Over one hundred years ago, on July 1, all the provinces—regions similar to states—were united under one government. This was called the Dominion of Canada. Canada Day honors this official birthday of the country.

Canadians enjoy many patriotic programs and activities on this day. The country's beautiful flag—the Canadian Red Ensign—is flown from public buildings, business places, schoolhouses, and many homes. Patriotic songs such as "O, Canada" and "God Save the Queen" are sung. The national symbol of Canada, the Maple leaf, is proudly displayed.

On July 1 remember to say, "Happy Birthday, Canada!"

A Fourth of July Family Party

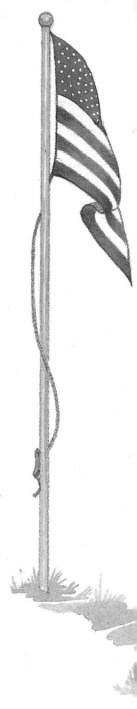

Every Fourth of July Sam's family had a big get-together. They called it the summertime family reunion.

This Fourth it was to take place at Sam's house. First Sam's mother called everyone to be sure they were coming. Sam's four grandparents, two uncles, three aunts, and a dozen cousins all said they would come. What fun it was to get ready for them.

"I'm not sure I can remember the names of all my cousins," Sam said to his mother.

"We'll make a rhyme of it," his mother told him. After awhile, she recited:

> *A Dozen Cousins* (that's 12, you know)
> Alice, Linda, Sharon, Peter, David, Karen,
> Kitty, Billy, Nick, Carol, Mary, and Dick.

They repeated the rhyme until Sam knew it.

"Now if I can only remember which name goes with which cousin," he said.

The Fourth of July was a bright, sunny day. Early in the morning Sam and his father put out the flag to celebrate the birthday of the country. By noon everyone had arrived. They brought baskets of fried chicken, salads, baked beans, cakes, cookies, lemonade, and even ice cream. What a feast! What a reunion!

When everyone had eaten, they played a game of baseball.

And when the day was over, Sam knew he would never forget which name went with which cousin.

A Nature Walk with Sally and Sam

Near Sally and Sam's neighborhood was a place called Little Big Woods. One midsummer day early in August, Mary, an older girl who lived nearby, asked Sally and Sam's mothers if she could take them on a nature walk.

"Of course," said Sally's mother, and gave them each an apple in case they got hungry.

"Of course," said Sam's mother, and gave them cookies to go with the apples.

"Let's take the path that leads to Silver Brook," Mary said. And so they started off on their nature walk.

They hadn't gone far when Sam stopped them. "Look!" he whispered. "What's that?"

Mary whispered back, "It's a young woodchuck. It's also called a groundhog. Leave your apple core by the path. It loves fruit."

Farther along, Mary told them to stop.

"On that tree over there is a vine you must stay away from," she warned. "It's poison ivy. The shiny green leaf has three leaflets. Poison ivy gives you an itchy rash if you touch it."

At Silver Brook they saw tiny fish. Mary said they were minnows. On the way home Sally and Sam practiced remembering the names of all the wild flowers they had seen.

It was an interesting nature walk, and it was twice as interesting when they told their mothers all about it. They could hardly wait to take the walk again. Would you like to go on such a walk?

Signs and Sounds of Autumn

Green leaves change to red and gold.
Once more the school bells chime.
Corn is waiting in the field
For farmers' harvest time.

Crowds are cheering football games.
Cider's cold and sweet,
And jack-o'-lanterns brightly smile
As you say, "Trick or treat."

Thanksgiving holidays arrive,
And we can all agree
That autumn is a thankful time—
Just right for you and me.

The First Day of School

Sally and Sam's friends were starting school.

There was a new first grade teacher. Miss Gladstone, who had taught first grade for years, would not be back, and no one knew anything about the new teacher.

"I hope the new teacher isn't cross," Tony said.

"I hope the new teacher is pretty," Martha said.

"I hope she won't make us work too hard," Tom said.

When they returned from the first day of school, they were full of good news.

"She has a nice smile," Tony said.

"She's pretty," Martha said.

"I don't have any homework to do," Tom said.

School was off to a good start.

Things to Do

Remember in September:

    The first Monday is a holiday that we call Labor Day. It honors working people. It is fun to watch a Labor Day parade.

October brings a lot of things to do:

    Gather brightly colored leaves and press them.

    Help rake the leaves as they fall from the trees.

    Take a pumpkin trip and pick one out to make a jack-o-lantern.

    Bring in the outdoor plants before Jack Frost gets them.

    It is apple harvest time. Eat one!

Remember in November:

    Think of all the things you have to be thankful for at Thanksgiving. Learn a Thanksgiving thank-you.

    Children's Book Week is in November. What is your favorite storybook?

Thanksgiving

Sally's family planned to go to Grandmother and Grandfather Brown's home for Thanksgiving.

Sam's family planned to drive to Grandmother and Grandfather Lane's home for Thanksgiving.

Then, on the day before Thanksgiving, came the first big snow of the season. The snow came down faster and faster. The wind howled and blew the snow into big drifts. Sally's father came home from work early.

"We're so glad to have you home safe and sound," Sally's mother said.

"I'm afraid I have bad news," Sally's father said. "I telephoned Grandmother and Grandfather Brown. The storm is even worse where they live. We won't be able to go there for Thanksgiving."

Sally tried not to cry, but she was very, very disappointed.

The same thing happened at Sam's house. There was no chance they could drive to his grandparents' home.

Sally's mother had a good idea. She

telephoned Sam's mother. When she finished talking, she turned to Sally.

"Sam and his parents are coming here for Thanksgiving dinner," she said. "We'll have fun. Just you wait and see."

Next day, while they waited for dinner, Sam's father said, "When I was a little boy, my father always told the story of the first Thanksgiving."

"Tell us," Sam and Sally said at the same time.

So Sam's father told them about the Pilgrims and how,

many years ago, this small group of people crossed a stormy ocean and came to a new land. The first year for them was bad, but friendly Indians helped them. Things got better, and at year's end the Pilgrims had a feast. They invited the Indians and gave thanks for their dinner and their new home. It was the first Thanksgiving.

"It's our first Thanksgiving together," Sam said, "and I'm thankful."

"So am I," Sally added. "Happy Thanksgiving, everyone!"

NOTE TO PARENTS

It is important to help children notice the changes in nature as one season follows another. The outdoors is a big picture book illustrating winter, spring, summer, and fall.

You can point out the signs and sounds of each season. As you do this, you introduce the concepts of time and change. With your help, your children will learn to observe the wonderful world around them. Gradually, not only the names of the seasons will be learned but the names of the months, too.

Stories, pictures, and songs can reinforce this. Holidays of the various seasons are treasured times of family togetherness. They are doors that open to wider rooms of happiness and love.

These are precious years. Make the most of them.

Word Games

The Thinking Word Game: You can play this game with your mother, father, a friend, or alone. Answer these questions with as many words as you can.

Can you think of some WET words?
(Samples: water, rain, swimmer.)

Can you think of some HEAVY words?
(Samples: elephant, truck, big rock.)

Can you think of some COLD words?
(Samples: ice, snow, winter.)

Can you think of some NOISY words?
(Samples: honk, bang, toot.)

Can you think of some TALL words?
(Samples: giraffe, giant, tree.)

Matching Words with Pictures: With your mother or father, go through some old magazines. Find and cut out ten things you know well, such as pictures of boys, girls, cars, books, cats, pigs, or men. Now ask your mother or father to print on ten small cards the words for the pictures you have cut out. Mix up words and pictures and then match them.

The Alphabet Word Game: Two players or more are best for this game, though you can play it alone. The first player says, "I am *A*," and names three words that begin with A, such as ape, astronaut, and apple.

The next player says, "I am *B*," and names three B words. In this way, the players proceed through the alphabet.

When someone cannot think of three words for a letter, that person is out of the game. *X* and *Z* words can be hard to think of. Just naming one word starting with those letters is better. If any of the players go through all the letters of the alphabet, start again at the beginning. Remember, though, you should not use the same word twice in a game.

The Sound Alike Game: Two or more can play this rhyming game. Ask someone to make the following sound cards: A (as in *say, day, hay*), AT (as in *bat, cat, hat*), ED (as in *bed, head, red*), IK (as in *stick, brick, trick*), O (as in *go, no, toe*), and U (as in *blew, boo!, chew*).

Deal out the cards to the players. The first player holds up a card and says the sound. The next player must say a word that rhymes with that sound, and so on, until no more rhyme words can be thought of. Then the second player says the word sound on a card, and the game continues. Stop when too many players get tired.

Five Fairy Tale Riddles

Riddle Number One:

In the woods I found a house,

And tiptoed in just like a mouse.

I sipped some soup and sat in three chairs,

Then went to sleep in a bed upstairs,

And when I awakened I saw three bears!

Who am I?

Riddle Number Two:

For five little beans I sold a cow,

And here is what happened, then

and now.

There grew a beanstalk to the sky,

On which I climbed so very high.

I met a giant and on that day

Found a magic harp and got away.

Who am I?

Riddle Number Three:

I wore a cloak of brightest red.

I had a Grandma sick in bed.

I took her cakes on a certain day,

And met a wolf along the way.

Who am I?

Riddle Number Four:

Seven very little men

Let me safely stay with them.

I kept their cottage nice and neat,

And cooked for them good things to

eat.

To help you get the answer right—

My name rhymes well with *low* and

bright.

Who am I?

Riddle Number Five:

Most everyone made fun of me—

The ugliest thing they ever did see.

I flew away 'cause I felt so bad—

Cold and hungry—life was bad.

But lo, and behold! when winter was

gone,

I had become a beautiful swan.

Who was I?

Here are the answers all in a row. How many riddles did you know?

Goldilocks • Jack • Red Riding Hood • Snow White • Ugly Duckling

A Word-and-Picture Story

In this word-and-picture story, you will meet a flower 🌼 , a ladybug 🐞 , a toad 🐸 , a bumblebee 🐝 , a butterfly 🦋 , and a hummingbird 🐦 .

Each time you see one of these pictures, say the word it stands for.

The Sad Little 🌼

Once upon a summer day there was a sad little 🌼 . The 🌼 was all alone except for a 🐞 who kept flying home to see her children. "I'm so lonely," said the sad little 🌼 .

"I'm here," croaked a little green 🐸 , sitting underneath the little 🌼 .

"But you keep hopping away," the 🌼 said to the little green 🐸 .

"That's because I'm so busy," the 🐸 said, as he hopped away.

A big 🐝 buzzed close to the little 🌼 . "You're

very sweet today," the big 🐝 said to the little 🌼 ,
"but I must buzz along."

A pretty 🦋 flitted around the 🌼 , and a 🐦
stopped long enough to say hello. Then the 🐦 and the
🦋 both flew away.

"Oh, my!" said the little 🌼 . "All my friends can
come and go, but I must stay in one place." Just then the
🌼 heard a soft hello. The warm sun had caused another
🌼 to bloom, and another 🌼 , and another 🌼 . The
🐝 came back to visit each 🌼 , and so did 🦋 , and
🐞 , and 🐦 .

Little 🌼 was now a happy little 🌼 with so
many friends close by.

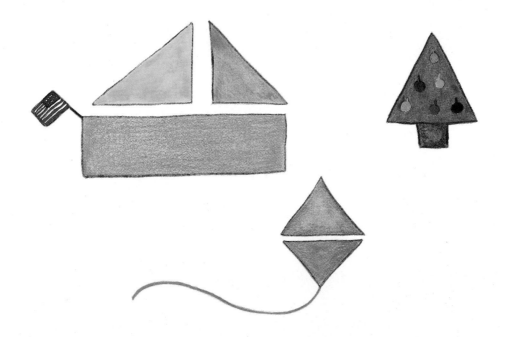

173

All words are important but sometimes name words are the most important of all, as this story points out.

Rumpelstiltskin

There was once a poor woodchopper who had a most beautiful daughter. One day when he delivered wood to the king's palace, the king spoke to him. The woodchopper, wanting to sound important, said, "Your Majesty, I have a daughter who can spin straw into gold."

"Really," the king said, "that's remarkable. Bring your daughter to me."

When the beautiful daughter arrived, she was taken to a room filled with straw. The king gave her a spinning wheel. "Get to work," he told her. "If by morning you have not spun the straw into gold, you will have to live here in this room." He closed the door, and the girl was alone.

Since she did not know how to turn straw to gold, she began to weep. Suddenly, a strange little man appeared before her. "What will you give me to spin the straw into gold?" he asked.

"My necklace," the girl answered. He took the necklace and sat down behind the spinning wheel. By morning he had spun all the straw into gold.

The king was delighted, but he was also greedy. He took her to a larger room filled with even more straw. "Change it into gold," he said and left.

Again the little man appeared. This time she gave him the ring on her finger. By morning all the straw was turned into gold.

When the king saw the gold, he took the girl to a larger room with more straw. "If you can spin all this straw into gold, you will become my queen," he said.

Once more the little man appeared. This time she had nothing to give him. "Promise to give me your first child if you become queen," he said.

She promised.

The gold was waiting for the king next morning, and he was so pleased that he did indeed marry her.

In time the queen had a beautiful baby. Soon the little man arrived and demanded the child. The queen began weeping. Feeling sorry for her, the little man said, "If within three days you can tell me what my name is, you may keep the child."

When he returned the first night, the queen had a long list of names ready. "Fred. Peter. Charles," she said, along with all the other names on the list. Not one was right.

The next day she gathered all the odd names anyone had ever heard. When the little man appeared, she recited, "Gravyface. Dogbiscuit. Buzzardwings." And on and on and on. Again she failed.

Before the little man arrived on the third night, a messenger came to the queen. "Today, deep in the wood," he said, "I saw an odd little man dancing, and as he danced he sang these words:

> The time is drawing very near
>
> And soon the queen's child will be here—
>
> Cause no one ever will exclaim
>
> That Rumpelstiltskin is my name!

The queen smiled and thanked the messenger. When the little man appeared that night, she asked him, "Is

Tommy your name?" He shook his head.

"Is Eddie your name?"

"No, no," he answered.

"Then—it must be Rumpelstiltskin," the queen said.
The little man howled with rage and ran away, never
to be heard of again.

The queen, the king, and their beautiful baby lived
happily ever after.

Acting Out a Story

Stories are fun to act out. Choose a story you know well and make a play of it, just like you see on television. For instance, the story of Noah's ark is one you might select.

You can pretend that you are different animals walking up the bridge that leads to Noah's ark.

Are you a slinky tiger?

Are you a big, shaggy bear?

Or a shy deer?

A funny monkey?

A curious raccoon?

A hopping rabbit?

A chattering squirrel?

You may give the different parts to friends. If you are by yourself, you can act out all the different animals. It is fun to play games all by yourself when you do not have a friend to play with.

Maybe you will want to add a storyteller to tell what is happening. The storyteller might be Noah himself.

Some other favorite stories that are fun to act out are the stories of Cinderella, Goldilocks, the three Little Pigs, and Red Riding Hood.

Meet These Words

Here are words helpful to know

That come in handy wherever you go!

IN
OUT

UP
DOWN

RIGHT
LEFT

ON
OFF

TELEPHONE

PAY HERE

U.S. MAIL

REST ROOMS

GIRLS

BOYS

Watch out! Words meant for you

For pointing out WHAT NOT TO DO!

STAY OFF THE GRASS

WET PAINT

DO NOT TOUCH

DO NOT LITTER

QUIET, PLEASE

DANGER

MEN AT WORK

BEWARE THE DOG

THIN ICE—NO SKATING

Another good place to meet words is the SUPERMARKET

and, best of all, in BOOKS!

Making Your Own Book

The first step in making a book is deciding what to put in it. Most books are made up of words and pictures. You can draw your own pictures, or you can use pictures from old magazines, catalogs, or travel folders.

You may want to have a special kind of book. Here are some ideas for special books:

1. A book about animals
2. A book about trucks and cars
3. A book about flowers
4. A holiday book
5. A book about the things in your house
6. An alphabet book
7. A book about good things to eat
8. A book about the work that people do
9. A book about how to be healthy
10. A book about birds

An easy way to make a book is to take several sheets of paper of the same size. If you wish, find two heavier sheets of paper. These can be the front and back, or the covers, of the book.

When you have decided on the number of pages you want in your book, ask your mother or father to make two holes near the edge of each page. Be sure the holes are in the same places on all the pages.

Before you tie the pages together, choose or draw the pictures you want in your book. If you have cut-out pictures, put one or two, according to how big they are, on each page. If you draw your own pictures, the size and number on each page are up to you.

Tell your mother or father what you want to say under each picture. They can write or print it for you.

Thinking of a title, or name, for your book is next. You may want to call it MY BOOK, or you may want to think of other titles. Under the title of the book, you should have your name because you are the *author*. An author is a person who writes books.

Now find a ribbon, a shoelace, or a piece of string for tying the pages together.

Your book is done! Isn't it fun to have a book of your very own to look at and to show to others?

Sally and Sam's Favorite Nursery Rhymes

Mary's Little Lamb

Mary had a little lamb,
    Its fleece was white as snow,
And everywhere that Mary went
    The lamb was sure to go.

It followed her to school one day,
    Which was against the rule;
It made the children laugh and play
    To see a lamb at school.

Jack Be Nimble

Jack be nimble,
Jack be quick,
Jack jump over
The candlestick.

182

Queen
of
Hearts

The Queen of Hearts,

She made some tarts,

All on a summer's day.

The Knave of Hearts,

He stole the tarts

And took them clean away.

The King of Hearts

Called for the tarts

And beat the Knave full sore.

The Knave of Hearts

Brought back the tarts

And vowed he'd steal no more.

Little Piggie

This little pig went to market.

This little pig stayed at home.

This little pig had roast beef.

This little pig had none.

This little pig cried,

    "Wee, wee, wee!

I can't find my way home!"

To Market, to Market

To market, to market, to buy a fat pig.

Home again, home again, dancing a jig.

To market, to market, to buy a fat hog.

Home again, home again, jiggety-jog.

Hickory, Dickory, Dock

Hickory, dickory, dock!

The mouse ran up the clock.

The clock struck one

And down he run,

Hickory, dickory, dock!

Old King Cole

Old King Cole
Was a merry old soul,
And a merry old soul was he.
He called for his pipe
And he called for his bowl
And he called for his fiddlers three.
Every fiddler he had a fine fiddle,
And a very fine fiddle had he.
Oh, there's none so rare
As can compare
With King Cole and his fiddlers three.

Peter Piper

Peter Piper picked a peck of pickled peppers.
A peck of pickled peppers Peter Piper picked.
If Peter Piper picked a peck of pickled peppers,
Where's the peck of pickled peppers Peter Piper picked?

Little Bo-Peep

Little Bo-Peep has lost her sheep
And can't tell where to find them;
Leave them alone, and they'll come home
And bring their tails behind them.
Little Bo-Peep fell fast asleep
And dreamt she heard them bleating.
But when she awoke, she found it a joke,
For they still were a-fleeting.
Then up she took her little crook,
Determined for to find them.
She found them indeed,
But it made her heart bleed,
For they'd left all their tails behind 'em.

Baa, Baa, Black Sheep

Baa, baa, Black Sheep,
Have you any wool?
Yes, sir; yes, sir; three bags full.
One for my Master, one for my Dame,
And one for the little boy
That lives down the lane.

Humpty Dumpty

Humpty Dumpty sat on a wall.

Humpty Dumpty had a great fall.

All the King's horses,

And all the King's men

Couldn't put Humpty Dumpty together again.

Old Mother Hubbard

Old Mother Hubbard

Went to the cupboard

To get her poor dog a bone.

But when she got there

The cupboard was bare,

And so the poor dog had none.

Wee Willie Winkie

Wee Willie Winkie runs through the town,

Upstairs and downstairs in his nightgown,

Rapping at the window,

Crying through the lock,

"Are the children in their beds,

For now it's eight o'clock?"

The Lion and the Mouse

Mighty lion, king of the jungle, was sound asleep in his den. A small mouse had lost her way and in her fright scampered across the lion's huge paw. With a surprised roar, the lion awakened. Annoyed at having his nap disturbed, he grabbed the mouse and held her under his paw.

"Oh, please, sir," squeaked the mouse, "I meant no harm. I know you could hurt me with a flick of your paw, but please let me go. If you do, I promise to do a good turn for you someday."

The lion smiled at the idea that such a tiny creature could ever help him. "Go your way," he said. "Don't bother me again." He went back to sleep.

Some time later the lion was walking in the jungle, as a lion often does, when he was caught in a rope net that hunters had set as a trap. He turned this way and that way, becoming more tangled up than ever. His roars of anger echoed throughout the jungle.

Not far away the mouse heard the roars. "My friend lion must be in trouble," she said, and hurried toward him. "Don't worry," she told the lion when she saw that he was trapped. "I'll help you!" With her small, sharp teeth, she gnawed through the ropes, one by one, until the lion was able to get free.

So the lion escaped, and the mouse made good her promise to repay the lion for sparing her life.

Whether you are big or little, you can help others.

Sam's Favorite Fable
The Hare and the Tortoise

Once upon a time there was a hare who went about telling everyone over and over again how speedy he was. He also made a lot of fun of a tortoise who lived nearby in the meadow. The tortoise was a slow but steady fellow, well liked by all the animals. "What a slowpoke," the hare said to the tortoise one summer day. "Honestly, if I crept around like you, I'd be ashamed of myself."

"I may not be so fast," the tortoise said, "but in the long run I get there."

"You want to have a race?" the hare asked the tortoise, and ran in circles around him.

The tortoise was very annoyed. "Sure. I'll race you." The other meadow animals were amazed, and, in truth, the tortoise was too. It had been a silly thing for him to say, but he felt that he had to stand by his word.

So a race was arranged between the tortoise and the hare, all the way across the meadow to the top of the hill. A crow offered to be the judge and flew to the hilltop. The hare and tortoise came to the starting line, and a happy chipmunk started the race.

The tortoise crawled on his way, and the hare raced ahead of him and was soon out of sight. The day was hot and when the hare came to a shady spot, he looked back at the tortoise, who was far behind. "I'll just rest here for a while," he said. "No hurry!"

When the tortoise crawled past him, the hare was fast asleep. The tortoise saw him and pushed on.

After a long nap, the hare woke up. "Better speed on," he said and hopped toward the hilltop. But he was too late. The tortoise inching steadily forward had already reached the finish line.

"The tortoise is the winner," Judge Crow announced. "Slow but steady won!"

The race does not always go to the swift.

The Goodbye Page

This is the last page of your book, but it is only the beginning of interesting things for you to do.

You may want to put up a bulletin board in your favorite spot. On it you can place pictures that you like, or things you collect, or special things you want to remember.

A famous poet, Robert Louis Stevenson, wrote:

"The world is so full of a number of things,

I'm sure we should all be as happy as kings."

There are many adventures ahead for you. Think of all the books there are to discover, music to hear, places to go, things to see and do. Every day will have its pleasures and surprises.

Have happy times!

NOTE TO PARENTS

This last section, *Fun with Words,* has been a reading readiness exercise and also a review.

The ability to read well and to understand well is the biggest step toward success in learning.

The word games, riddles, suggestions for acting out stories are ways of stretching the imagination. Some of these features are for younger children; some for older. If your children do not understand certain words, show them what a help a dictionary can be.